Kalilah and Dimnah

Juan de la Cuesta
Hispanic Monographs

Kalilah and Dimnah

An English Version of Bidpai's Fables
Based upon Ancient Arabic and Spanish Manuscripts

by

THOMAS BALLANTINE IRVING

University of Tennessee, Knoxville

Juan de la Cuesta
Newark, Delaware

The cover images: (front) *Kalila visits the captive Dimna*,
Herat, 1430, Revan 1022, folio 56a;
(back) *Lion attacking a Bull*, Herat, 1430, Revan 1022, folio 46b.
The Topkapi Palace Museum, Turkey.

The large decorated capital letters which begin each chapter are from Juan de la
Cuesta's stock of type from his seventeenth century Madrid print shop. We are indebted
to Professor R.M. Flores of the University of British Columbia for providing these.

TABLE OF CONTENTS

❧ Introduction ❧

THE COLLECTION of fables entitled *Kalīlah wa-Dimnah*, or *Bidpai's Fables** originated chiefly in India, where the nucleus of the collection is known under the name *Panchatantra* or the "Five Books." According to the Sanskrit introduction, the stories were used for training young princes in wise conduct, although the morality is much more practical than idealistic.

The stories arose from a realm of Indian folktale which became connected, both in Brahamanism and especially in Buddhism, with the doctrine of metempsychosis, so that the animals are considered as being in various stages of transmigration and many times reflect human attributes. That explains why characters seem to be only masked humans, and this can be understood when we remember that the Indians can regard them as souls on the road to a higher life.

The tales have migrated over most of the globe, both East and West of India. The route that interests us is the one which brought the fables into Persia. Whether the stories reached the Pahlavi (i.e., Middle Persian) in a Buddhist, Brahamanic, or Jain version is not our problem. The chief point is that their thought-pattern was Indian, and that even when they reached the West in the Spanish version, traces of this outlook are stil to be found.

Almost a dozen stories have been added since the original "Five Books" or chapters of the primitive *Panchatantra*; these added chapters are the present Chapter II (Dimnah's Trial), and Chapters VII

---

*The name Bidpai is merely the Arabic (via the Old Persian) transliteration of Vidyāpati, which in Sanskrit means 'chief sage' or 'scholar'. Thus the second phrase of the opening sentence of this book: "Bidpai his chief philosopher" is really a redundant expression. Such sages were typically tutors of the young princes at an Indian court, and the tales are their lesson material, just as Patronio served Count Lucanor.

till the end. In other words, the *Panchatantra* only comprises Chapters I, III, IV, V, and VI of our text; hence the Arabic and Spanish versions represent a considerably enhanced stock of fables.

The traditional translator from the Pahlavi into Arabic was ʿAbdallāh ibn-al-Muqaffaʿ, a Persian convert to Islam, who rendered the tales around 750 A.D., although the *Fihrist* (an Arabic encyclopedia of literature) suggests that Ibn-al-Muqaffaʿ may not have been the only translator from the Pahlavi. Keith-Falconer quotes al-Asmāʿi for Ibn-al-Muqaffaʿ's excellent Arabic, whereas Cheikho, the early twentieth century Lebanese Jesuit editor of what has in many ways become the Vulgate version of the Arabic, attributes some of the textual errors to the fact that Ibn-al-Muqaffaʿ was not an Arabic-speaking person by birth.

Ibn-al-Muqaffaʿ's version attained great popularity throughout the Near East, and was translated into Late Syriac, Hebrew, modern Persian, and Turkish. Keith-Falconer gives a description and a table of these and the European translations. The Persian translation was called *Anvár-i-Suhaylí* or the "Lights of Canopus," and it was a French translation of this work that La Fontaine used in the second edition of his *Fables*, as the Persian form Pilpai for Bidpai indicates. Cheikho even reports a poetical version of the stories in Arabic. It also seems likely that Arab traders carried portions of the fables to Africa, from where the Black man brought them to America where they developed into the Br'er Rabbit stories.

When Alfonso X, "The Scholar," set up his school of translators in Toledo in the middle of the thirteenth century, this famous collection was one of those works he chose to render into Castilian. Solalinde doubts whether Alfonso himself was the translator, but since he had a school working under his direction, I prefer to include it in the cycle of works which was published under his influence. Likewise it has often been questioned whether it was translated into Latin and then into Spanish, or directly into the Romance tongue; but Alemany's contention that we should correct the reading of Alfonso's statement that the work was translated into *latyn e romançado* (i.e., translated into Latin and then put into Romance) by suppressing the *e* so as to read that it was rendered into *latyn romançado* or Romance Latin, meaning the vernacular, seems to make more sense.

This conclusion is inevitable after any comparison of the two versions, Arabic and Castilian, since they concur to such an extent as to preclude any possibility of a third language intervening. The Spanish itself appears to follow an Arabic text so closely that it is an indispensable witness to an early state of the Arabic test in many places where the latter exhibits variants in its several present-day versions.

Calila e Digna was the first extensive piece of prose literature in the popular language of Spain, for it was most probably translated in the year 1251, while Alfonso was still heir to the throne. It is important chiefly because it marks a point of confluence in the streams of Arabic and Spanish civilization, and therefore affords us material for study of the direct influence of the former culture upon the latter, in both the linguistic and the literary domain.

Between the years 1263 and 1278, shortly after this Spanish translation was done, John of Capua, a converted Jew, made a Latin translation of a Hebrew version that a certain Rabbi Joel had done in the early part of the thirteenth centrury. He called this Latin version the *Directorium Vitae Humanae*. It achieved wider popularity than the Alfonsine work, and was itself subsequently translated into most European languages, ultimately being printed in a Spanish rendering at Zaragoza in 1493. Working from an Italian version, Sir Thomas North, the translator of Plutarch's *Lives*, rendered it into English in 1569 or 1570 as the *Morall Philosophie of Doni* (after Doni, the Italian transiator from the Latin). By this time we are, of course, dealing with texts which have diverged a great deal from the Arabic.

In 1315 Raymond de Béziers made another Latin translation, evidently basing it upon both the Alfonsine and the Capuan works; but this version, like the Alfonsine, failed to achieve the popularity of the *Directorium* or the Eastern *Kalīlah*. A little known English version was made in 1819 from de Sacy's Arabic edition by the Rev. Wyndham Knatchbull. This translation is good, although it suffers the faults of the edition upon which it was based.

Thus this stream of tales which originated in the *Panchatantra* of India and was enriched by passing through Persian and Arabic, found its was into European literature; whether in single fables like "The Dog and his Shadow" or "The Talkative Tortoise," in collections of fables or tales like La Fontaine's or Straparola's, or into cycles like Reynard the Fox and Br'er Rabbit.

One important point that does not seem to have been studied fully is the relation between the practical ethics of *Kalīlah* and that of the picaresque novel. To be sure, Menéndez y Pelayo and González Palencia both pointed out the affinity of the Maqāmāt or Arabic baroque picaresque narrative to the pícaro literature, but no detailed study has as yet been completed in this field.

ఄ ఄ ఄ

The bibliography of studies of the Alfonsine version in modern times may be said to open in 1775 with Sarmiento's description in his *Memorial para la historia de la poesía y poetas españoles* in which he describes three extant manuscripts, one of which is now lost. Gayangos first published the text in 1860 from the two Escorial manuscripts, and in 1906 Allen edited a critical text based upon MS. A, and including the many variants from MS. B; this is the edition I have used in establishing the Spanish part of the present version.

However, we possess neither the original text nor yet a faithful copy of the Old Spanish version of *Calila e Digna*, nor of the Arabic text which must have been utilized by the Toledan translators. Therefore in our comparative studies, we must endeavor to reconstruct both Arabic and Spanish originals as accurately as possible. This is the motive of this edition.

The lost Arabic text used in Toledo is here reconstructed primarily on the basis of the standard Arabic text, *La version arabe de Kalīlah et Dimnah*, edited by Louis Cheikho, as has been the practice followed by other workers in the field, notably Alemany and Dietrich. Cheikho's text is based on a manuscript dated 739 A.H. (1539 A.D.).

This text has been collated with that of Khalīl al-Yāziji published in Beirut in 1888. Al-Yāziji's text is a complete one deriving from several printed models that have circulated throughout the Near East and Europe in the past century and a half and is provided with complete vowel-pointing. In general it is not as reliable as Cheikho, but there are several cases where it may be closest to the primitive form, since the Spanish supports it against the other

Arabic versions. Whenever it appears superior to Cheikho's, its variants have been used.

There is yet another Arabic version, ʿAzzam's 1941 Cairo edition based on the Aya Sofia manuscript, dating apparently from A.H. 618 (1221 A.D.). Since the pedagogical purpose of our edition appears well-served by Cheikho and Al-Yāziji, we have not incorporated the ʿAzzam edition here, but we encourage our readers, if they delve further into the subject of this book, to consult it.

One must bear in mind as well that none of these versions is the same as the copy we presume the Toledan translators used; and it is only through collation of representative models that we can conjecture what this Alfonsine original must have been. In addition to both Cheikho and Al-Yāziji, we have the Spanish MS. A (supplemented with variants from MS. B), which, as we have shown, furnish evidence for reconstructing the lost orignial. Keller and Linker's 1967 edition transcribes both Spanish manuscripts in their entirety, thus avoiding the confusion which may result from the innumerable variants in Allen's edition.

The two Spanish manuscripts supplement each other in much the same manner as the Arabic editions, although MS. B was collated at an early date with John of Capua's *Directorium* by some unknown author, and hence is less pure. The readings wherein these manuscripts do not mutually agree can most often be attributed to scribal errors, except where MS. B seems to have been thus influenced by the *Directorium*. MS. A, the better of these texts, forms the basis of Allen's work, whereas MS. B enables one to follow the narrative when the former falls short. Allen's collation has been accepted substantially for this study, except in such places as the Arabic versions indicate that his reading was erroneous.

Alemany has done us the service of collating the Spanish MS. A with his Spanish translation of Cheikho and Al-Yāziji, although one cannot trust him entirely in this matter and must work independently of his translation, especially where the Arabic and English idiom comes into play. Nonetheless, it is a valuable piece of work for those who care to penetrate further in the line of this study and are hampered by an insufficient command of Arabic. García Solalinde has published a literary edition of the Allen-Alemany Spanish text which is not as valuable for scholarly purposes, although Edgerton used it for his work.

What I have endeavored to do here is offer to the English speaking public as complete a version, from as many sources, and in as readable and comprehensible a form as possible, of *Kalilah and Dimnah*. A perfect scholarly collation, especially where more than one language is concerned, is obviously impossible—there are too many missing pieces in the linguistic and cultural labyrinth which is the history of this work. Nonetheless, its overwhelming importance, coupled with the scarcity of English versions, have made the preparation of this edition imperative, and I hope that it will prove of use to those who cannot consult the Arabic and Spanish versions in the original languages.

To the Reader

Cheikho's Arabic text forms the basis for the present translation. Where other sources were preferable they have been used, and placed between ⸢supershift parentheses;⸣ the inserted text is identified (according to the table on the next page) just before the close parentheses. Three types of textual insertions are most common: 1) Sections from al-Yāzigi, 2) Sections from the Old Spanish texts, and 3) sections where *Calila e Digna* and al-Yāzigi support each other against Cheikho. The translator's own insertions are naturally enclosed [in square brackets.]

Table of Abbreviations

List of Spellings

I am suppressing diacritical marks on Arabic words in the body of the narrative, but offer here a table of proper spellings of these words in transliteration.

Aylādh	Jarkān	Nūshīrwān
Barājūn	Jawīr	Qāradīn
Brahmūn	Kāl	Qarīdūn
Būrkhasht	Kalīlah	Qarūnād
Burzōē	Kanān Abzūn	Rāmharān
Dabshalīm	Kasrūn	Rūmī
Dastabā	Khayār	Sakhīn
dīnār	Kūraqānah	Shādaram
Fayrūz	Maliāropya	Tātharūn
Garuḍa	Manūd	Ṭitawāy
Ḥabal	Mārūt	ṭiṭṭibha
Hamyūn	Maṭūn	Viṣṇu
Īrīkhat	Niaçor	Zīrak

Chapter [I]

Of the Lion and the Bull

[Or How to Lose Friends]

 ABSHALIM, THE KING of India, said to Bidpai, 'his⁽ᴾ⁾ chief philosopher: "Make me up a fable about two men who love each other, and how a swindling liar comes between them and incites them to be enemies."

Bidpai said: "Whenever it happens that a lying swindler comes between two men who love each other, they then break up their friendship and are at odds with each other. One of these fables is as follows:

IN THE LAND of Dastaba there lived a wealthy merchant who had 'three'ⁿ sons. When they came of age, they hastened to squander their father's money and practiced no trade by which they could earn any wealth. So he took them to task and warned them; and this is part of the warning that he gave them:
"My sons, the worldly man seeks three things which he can never achieve without four other things. The three things sought are an easy living, rank among men, and success in the hereafter. The four things without which you cannot attain these three are: earning money honestly; then, taking care of the principal you have earned and keeping a clear account of it; next, knowing how much to budget for honest expenditures, a living for your family and relatives, and something to benefit them in the after life; and, finally, keeping enough to tide you over all the hard knocks that may come up.

"Whoever neglects any of these four factors will never achieve nor earn what he wants nor become wealthy enough to live off it. For even if he is wealthy and earns a great deal, his wealth will be of no avail to him and he will be unable to take care of the principal, so that he will soon use it up and have nothing left over; it will all disappear and never benefit him. He will not be able to prevent his little from leaving him, like eyeshadow, which eventually vanishes even if you use only a speck of it at a time.

"But even if he earns and keeps track of it, sees it bears interest, and does not fritter it away in sundry ways when it might otherwise be useful, people will think him poor and penniless, and he won't be able to keep it from slipping away and leaving him when he most wants it, as in misfortune and illness; like the cistern which has water constantly pouring into it, and because there is no way to use it up nor any outlet for it to escape, the weight of the increase breaks down where it is not solid and the water runs away, creating havoc in its wake."

Then the merchant's sons took their father's advice and heeded his command. The eldest went off on business towards the land called Manud. On his way he passed by a spot where there was a great deal of mud. Now he had a cart pulled by two bulls, one called Shatrabah and the other Bandabah. Shatrabah fell in the mud, and the man and his helpers worked away till they got him out. Afterwards he was so overcome by fatigue that the merchant left a man behind with him, ordering him to stay some days and when he saw he was well to catch up with him.

The very next day the man got disgusted with the place, and overtook the merchant, abandoning the bull. He informed him that the bull had died; ⁽adding:ⁿ

[A. The Man Beset with Perils]

⁽"When a man's hour is come and the day of his death is at hand, none of his precautions can arrest the arm uplifted to strike him, his labor is in vain, and his exertions are a mockery. He is like^Y the man who they say$^{Y/CeD}$ went into a wilderness abounding in wild beasts.

"The man well knew the byways of that country and what measures to take. Still he had not gone very far before he^Y saw a wolf[Y/CeD] from one of the packs. When the man noticed the wolf[Y] was advancing upon him,[Y/CeD] he became frightened and looked right and left to see if he could find some way of escape. He discovered only a village on the opposite side of a river,[Y] and ran[Y/CeD] towards it[Y] in haste.

"When he reached the river, he found[Y/CeD] that it had no[Y] bridge.[Y/CeD] He saw that[Y] the wolf was at his heels, and so he threw himself into the water[Y/CeD] although[Y] he was unable to swim. Here he would have drowned, had not some villagers observed him. They jumped in to the rescue, and dragged him out[Y/CeD] just as he was on the point of perishing.[Y]

"When the man was with them[Y/CeD] and no longer in peril of the wolf[Y] and the water,[Sp] he noticed an isolated house and said: 'I am going to go into this house and rest!'

"As he was entering it, he caught sight of a band of robbers who had waylaid a merchant on the highway. They were engaged in dividing up his wealth and preparing to kill him.

"When the man saw that, he feared for his life and went back to the village.[Y] He was leaning his back against a wall[Y/CeD] to catch his breath a moment from the shock and fatigue,[Y] when it fell down upon him and crushed him to death."[Y/CeD]

The merchant acknowledged the force of his servant's reasoning, but observed at the same time that the story was not new to him.[Kn]

While this was going on,[n] the bull hurried away from the spot and did not stop till he came to a well-watered and grassy meadow where he stayed. He was not long in putting on fat, and he roared and bellowed and lifted up his voice lustily.

Now a lion who was king of that region lived nearby, and he commanded many beasts of prey, like wolves, jackals, foxes, etc. The lion was conceited and obstinate in his opinions, while these were anything but perfect. So the lion heard the bull's roaring, and as he had not the slightest notion of what a bull was nor had ever heard one roar, he trembled from fear, while dreading lest his attendants should notice it. He stayed in one place and did not move anywhere.

Among those with him were two jackals, one called Kalilah and the other Dimnah. Both of them were well-bred and shrewd, although Dimnah was the worse of the two at heart and more given to violence; he was always on the lookout for the main chance, and though the lion did not know them, Dimnah said to Kalilah:[1]

"Don't you see, my friend, what a state the lion is in? He is staying in one spot without leaving it nor moving around as he usually does."

Kalilah said: "Why do you have to bother with what isn't your concern? Aren't we in good enough standing at the king's court,[2] finding what we need to eat? Don't we belong to the class that can talk to kings and observe their affairs? Keep quiet about this, for you know that whoever claims to say or do things that are not his business, has happen to him what happened to the monkey."

Dimnah said: "What was that?"

Kalilah said:

[B. The Inquisitive Monkey]

"Once upon a time a monkey was watching a carpenter splitting a beam with two wedges he had, sitting astride the wood like a rider on a horse. As often as he drove a wedge in, he moved forward.

"Then the carpenter got up and went out for something or other, and the monkey attempted to perform what was neither his trade nor his business. He got astride the beam with his back to the split and facing the wedge, so that his tail[3] hung down the crack. As he was working on the wedge, he tugged it out.

"When he tugged, the beam clapped shut on his tail and crushed it so that he fell down in a faint. He remained in that state until the carpenter came back. What happened to him from the carpenter in the way of blows and pain was even worse."

Dimnah said: "Well, I've heard your fable and understand it. However, you know that everyone who approaches kings does not come up just to fill his stomach, for stomachs can be filled anywhere; but one seeks such honor and rank as gladdens one's friends and grieves one's enemies. Only the vilest sort of people and the basest cowards are happy and content with cheap things, like the dog who finds a dry bone and is glad of it.

"Manly and prominent people are not satisfied with a little and do not consent to something small once something more suitable

comes along, just as a lion who is chasing a hare drops the rabbit
and goes after a wild ass once he catches sight of the latter. Don't
you see how a dog wags his tail a great deal till you throw him a
morsel; or how a rutting elephant who knows his own power and
strength does not eat choice fodder until he has been groomed and
cleaned?

"Now whoever lives other than in a most obscure position,
should have some idea of his own and his friends' merits, so that
even though his life is brief, it has been long. Whoever lives in
loneliness, sadness, and pettiness towards himself and his friends,
has a short life, no matter how long it lasts. For it has been said:
the wretch is one who ekes out his life in hardship; or again:
whoever worries only about his stomach is placed in the same cate-
gory as cattle or sheep."

Kalilah said: "I understand your argument; but return to your
senses! You know that every man has his own rank and ability,
and when he has found his level he should stick to it along with
those of his own standing. It is only right that he should be content and pleased with it. Besides, we don't have to step down from
any rank to reach the state we are in now."

Dimnah said: "Offices are really all held in common, and the
manly person finds out that his manliness raises him from humble
to exalted rank; while the unmanly individual lowers himself from
exalted to humble rank. Advancement from the lowest to the most
noble rank is a difficult and serious undertaking; while reduction
from nobility to humility is quite easy. An example of that is a
heavy stone which is hard to lift from the ground to one's
shoulder, while dropping it is easy. We ought to covet whatever
rank is above us with all our might, seeking it to the best of our
ability and not remaining in our present status if we can attain
another."

Kalilah said: "Well, what have you decided upon now?"

Dimnah said: "I want to explain this fright to the lion, for he is
weak-minded and is keeping his court uneasy about his command
over them. Perhaps at this stage I can get close enough to advise
the lion and attain rank and influence with him."

Kalilah said: "Whatever gave you the idea that the lion is
uneasy?"

Dimnah said: "I know that from my insight and intuition, for a person with insight often has the inside track on his friend's business just by what he sees; at times he knows it just from the other's appearance and gestures."

Kalilah said: "How do you hope for standing with the lion when you have never been a monarch's friend nor have any knowledge about serving, treating, nor even handling one?"

Dimnah said: "A big, strong, husky man always has enough strength for a heavy load, while a weakling cannot avail himself of guile the least bit. Traveling abroad does not harm the clever individual; nor can anyone turn aside the meek, smooth type."

Kalilah said: "A ruler generally does not honor the most distinguished people at his court, but chooses the one who gets closest to him. It is said that a king is like a vine which does not cling to the noblest tree, but only to whatever is closest. How can you hope for rank from the lion if you aren't near him?"

Dimnah said: "Of course I understand what you mean, for you are honest; but I know that those nearer the sovereign than we are weren't always in their present posts, but got closer and closer to him and finally reached office. Now I have an urge to reach their rank and position through my own efforts. It is said that no one stays long in a sovereign's court without coming up against much scorn, enduring hardship, holding his temper, and doing things for other people, till he reaches the highest rung of the ladder on his way up to the ruler."

Kalilah said: "I understand; but once you have reached the lion, what are you going to do with the rank you attain?"

Dimnah said: "Once I reach him and know his characteristics, then I'll play up to every whim and cater to his prejudices and little foibles. Whenever he wants something, I'll make it so attractive and encourage him in it, so that his pleasure will increase. Whenever he wants something I am afraid will harm or shame him, I'll show him how it can harm or shame him, and how dropping the matter will be useful and advantageous. I'll try to get this into his head gently and smoothly.

"I hope the lion will treat me better when he sees I am acting differently from others. For if the cultured and accomplished man wishes to separate falsehood from truth and truth from falsehood simultaneously, he does the same as the skillful artist who paints a picture on the wall so that it seems as though parts were stepping out of the wall and others to be walking into it, when they aren't. Thus when the lion notices my good points and recognizes them and whatever else I have to offer, he will be eager to ennoble me and keep me near him."

Kalilah said: "Since you have this idea, I am going to warn you against keeping company with a soverign; for his company is extremely dangerous. Wise men have said that there are three things which only a madcap should tackle, since only a few people come out of them: one is friendship with a monarch, another, drinking poison to test its effects, and [thirdly], trusting a woman with secrets. For wise men compare monarchs to a rugged mountain that is too steep to climb, and where there are all sorts of delicious fruits which feed only tigers. lions, wolves, and all kinds of wild beasts: climbing it is strenuous, while staying there is terrifying."

Dimnah said: "You are right in what you describe, except that whoever doesn't embark on dangers never reaches his heart's desire. Whoever drops a thing which may provide him with his needs through fear and dread of being upset, never achieves anything great. For it is said that three things cannot be attained without help or incurring trouble and the greatest risk: one is working with a monarch; another, trading at sea, and the other, fighting an enemy. Wise men have said: The accomplished and manly individual wants to be seen in only two places and nowhere else: with kings and honored, or with ascetics and serving God; like the elephant 'whose beauty and splendid appearance show up in only two places—in the desert fastness or as a mount for kings."[r]

Kalilah said: "May God grant you what you have resolved upon; but so far as I am concerned, I don't agree with this idea of yours."

So Dimnah went off to greet the lion.

The lion said to those around him: "Who is this?"

They said: "This is So-and-so, the son of So-and-so."

The lion said: "Why, I knew his father!"

So the lion walked up to him and said: "Where are you from?"

Dimnah said: "I have been hanging around the king's court in the hope that an occasion might arise where I might help him, for he often needs someone he doesn't notice. No one should be overlooked no matter how powerless or humble he seems, provided he has any use whatsoever; sometimes a piece of wood lying on the ground will help an itchy ear if you use it for scratching. If a creature knows the difference between advantage and disadvantage, you ought to use him."

When the lion heard Dimnah's words, he was surprised at them and thought he was giving him some sound advice. So he went over to his intimates and said: "If a man is virtuous and wise, though obscure and humble, then his virtue and intelligence should be pointed out and recognized, like the firebrand whose holder hides it while it must be displayed."

When Dimnah knew that the lion admired him, he said, "O king, your subjects and courtiers should be aware of flaunting however they feel towards you and standing upon too much ceremony. That is like grain such as wheat or barley or something else which lies hidden in the earth: one does not know what type it is until it comes up and may be seen. A sovereign ought to favor every man with the rank corresponding to his advice, insight, and whatever usefulness and good breeding he has. For it has been said that no one, not even a king, should place two things other than in their proper place nor keep them from their dignity; namely, ornaments for the feet and ornaments for the head.

Whoever sets a ruby or a pearl in lead, does not have any less of a pearl or a ruby for that, but just shows up his own ignorance. Thus is it said: Don't associate with a man who doesn't know his right side from his left. One never gets anything out of a man unless he is above him, from troops except from their command, nor out of religion except through its commentaries, scholars, and jurisprudents. For they say: Three things are superior in a very peculiar way, even though they sound almost the same: the vanquisher over the vanquished, the scholar over the schoolboy, and the speaker over the one spoken to.

"Most supporters, if they are not 'experienced,$^{\wp)}$ may cause harm in what they do. The outcome of an affair lies in the staunchness of its partisans, not in their numbers; like the man who wears a ruby whose weight is not great but still yields him what he needs. This is like a deed accomplished through gentleness; violence does not avail even though one is prepared to use it. A ruler should not despise an individual's manliness, no matter how humble his rank, for something small may be mighty and full of strength, just as a sinew taken from a dead body and used in a bow reaches its highest honor when a king employs it for his strength and prowess; or it is used in saddles and becomes a mount for kings and nobles.

Now Dimnah longed to attain dignity and honor with the king, and to let people know that it was not on account of the lion's previous acquaintance with 'his father'[η] but his own virtue and insight alone. So he said: "A sovereign is not intimate with men because they were intimate with their parents, nor keeps them at a distance because they were distant; but he honors each one according to his ability. There is nothing closer to a man than his body; but if some part of it becomes diseased, he does not get rid of the illness except with a medicine brought from afar. A rat is a neighbor in one's house, but when he starts to molest his enemy, he is driven off; the hawk is a wild beast, but when it becomes useful, it is cared for and tamed so that a king may carry it upon his hand."

When Dimnah finished talking, the king admired him even more and thanked him in reply. He said to those sitting with him: "A ruler should not try to injure an upright person, nor withhold a man from his rank; rather he should make amends for such past neglect, and not be lulled that a thing is past, but own up to it. In this people fall into two categories: one man is fundamentally of an easy-going disposition, like cold sandalwood which rapidly becomes hot and even dangerous when rubbed."

When Dimnah was on friendly terms with the lion, he took him aside and said to him: "I notice that the king is keeping to this one spot quite a while without leaving it. What is wrong?"

The lion said, since he did not want Dimnah to know that it was through cowardice on his part: "It isn't for 'fear."[Sp]

As they were chatting together, 'Shatrabah'[Y/CeD] the bull put forth a mighty bellow, which so startled the lion that he let Dimnah see clearly what was on his mind.

So he said: "I don't know what this voice is which I hear, except I think its owner's size must be in keeping, and his strength give the voice its power. If that's so, then this isn't the place for us!"

Dimnah said: "What if something else has upset the king?"

The lion said, "Nothing has upset me except the voice."

Dimnah said: "The king shouldn't leave his place once he has heard this noise, for it has been said: A weak dam is destroyed by water, intelligence by boasting, virtue by slander, and the weak heart by a loud voice and uproar. A certain fable has a statement that all noises should not be dreaded:

The lion said: "What is this fable?"

[C. The Hungry Fox and the Drum]

"Once upon a time there was a hungry fox going through a forest where a drum had been cast beside a tree. Whenever the wind blew, it moved the branches of the tree so that they hit the drum and made a loud noise.

"Now the fox heard that noise and went towards it until he reached the drum. When he saw it was big, he said to himself, 'It ought to be quite plump and meaty!'

"So he tried extremely hard until he burst it. When he saw how hollow it was, the fox said. 'Sometimes the vilest things have the biggest bodies and the strangest voices.'

"Now I have made this tale up for you in the hope that if this voice which frightened us[4] should reach us, we will find it less terrifying than we had imagined. If the king wants, he can send me to this voice while he stays here until I return with an explanation of the matter."

The lion agreed to his proposal and let him go. So Dimnah went towards the spot where the bull was.

When he had left the lion's company, the lion thought the matter over and regretted having sent Dimnah there. He said to himself. "I wasn't right in entrusting Dimnah with that; for if a man has been in a sovereign's court and incurs his ill favor without committing anything wrong, or has been recognized for his greed and gluttony; or if he is afflicted by harm or straitened circumstances and cannot return to normal, or some stroke has separated him from whatever power or wealth he possessed, or he was administering some work that was taken from him so that he was made much less important because of a partner's interference; or if he has committed some crime for which he fears some punishment, or is ill-disposed and does not love good; or if he remains in disgrace through some crime towards his peers, or he and his peers have gone through some test and should have some reward, or if some enemy he detests surpasses him in rank and esteem, or is untrustworthy in his observances and passions; or if he were expecting some advantage which turns out to be harmful, or wishes the sovereign's enemies well 'or to fight the latter's friends;"' all these people a ruler should not be in any hurry to trust, confide in, or rely upon."[5]

"Now Dimnah is a shrewd and cunning individual, but he has been looked down upon 'and ill-treated"' for so long that he may bear a grudge and be inclined to grieve and bother me. It may turn out that the owner of the voice is stronger and more powerful than I, and he may be longing to use and support him against me, thus hitting me below the belt."

The lion kept on thinking about this until he could not stand still, but hurried about, walking and sitting down and looking along the road until Dimnah hove in sight. When he saw him coming along alone, he felt calmer and went back to his spot; for he did not want Dimnah to think anything had made him leave his place.

When Dimnah entered the lion's presence, he said to him: "What did you accomplish?"

He said: "I saw a bull who has the voice you heard."

The lion said: "How strong is he?"

He said: "Nothing special; I went right up and spoke to him. I talked to him as an equal, and he couldn't do a thing to me!"

The lion said: "Don't let that fool you about him, nor lay it to weakness on his part! A strong wind does not crush weak grass, but mighty trees and castles. Likewise opposing captains do not attack privates, but challenge each other."

Dimnah said: "The king does not need to fear a thing from him nor 'to be distressed."' If your majesty wants me to fetch him to be your attentive and obedient servant, I shall do so."

The lion was glad at that, and said: "See here now, that is just what I want!"

Then Dimnah went off to the bull and told him without any fear or constraint: "The lion has sent me to bring you to him He ordered me to hurry back with you in an obedient frame of mind, so as to clear up your offense of not coming to see him soon enough and neglecting to call upon him. If you'll apologize, I'll hurry back to tell him so."

The bull said. "Who is this lion and where does he come from?"

Dimnah said. "He is king of the beasts of prey, and lives in such-and-such a place with his host of beasts."

Now the bull trembled at the mention of the lion and his beasts, and he said to Dimnah: "If you'll give me a safe-conduct, I'll go along with you."

Dimnah granted him the safe conduct, which reassured him. Then they both set off together and finally entered the lion's presence.

The lion treated the bull kindly, and asked him: "When did you reach this land, and what brought you to it?"

Shatrabah the bull related his story to him.

So the lion said: ⟨Be my companion$^{Y/CeD}$ and follower, and^{η} I'll honor and treat you kindly."

The bull paid his respects and thanked him. He stayed on, and the lion favored and honored him and became extremely fond of him. He tried him out and found he had insight and intelligence, and so he entrusted him with his secrets and consulted him about his affairs. During all the time he remained there, his admiration, attraction, and preference for him increased till he attained the highest rank among all his companions.

When Dimnah saw that the lion was keeping him exclusively to himself ahead of his other companions, and that he shared his private chamber and his conversations and pastimes, he envied him with all his heart and invented every sort ⟨of grievance^{η} against him. He grumbled to his brother Kalilah about it, and said. "Aren't you surprised at my ⟨bad judgment$^{Y/CeD}$ and weakness? What have I done except consider the lion's benefit and forget my own advantage until I spoiled it? Now I have finished with whatever rank I had!"

Kalilah said: "What happened to you is what happened to the ascetic."

Dimnah said: "What was that?"

Kalilah said:

[D. The Monk in the Underworld]

"Once upon a time a monk received a splendid suit of clothes from a certain king. A thief noticed it and began to covet the suit which the ascetic was wearing. So he went up to the monk ⟨and said:[Y/CeD] 'I want to accompany you so I may learn something from you and acquire some of your breeding.'

"So he went along with him, living exactly like the ascetic and serving the monk. He treated him in a friendly fashion as he waited upon him, and was patient until he got him off his guard. Then he took the suit and ran away with it.

When the ascetic missed both the man and the clothes, he knew it had been his companion. So he went looking for him, in order to confirm his suspicioons. In his search he finally approached the city of 'Mayat.[Sp]6

[D1. The Fox and the Goats]

"Along the road he chanced upon two mountain goats who were butting each other. They had been fighting so long that blood was streaming from them both.

"A fox came up to lap some of the blood, and while he was bent over, the goats rammed together on top of him, butting each other. Since he wasn't watching, they killed him.

[D2.The Whoremistress and her Slavegirl's Lover]

"So the monk went on till he came up to the city, and he entered it at nightfall. He didn't find any lodging nor shelter for the night except the house of a woman who was both a whore and a whoremistress, so he stopped with her.

"Now that woman had a slavegirl whom she used to hire out, but that girl had fallen for a man and didn't want to have any other. That reduced the woman's earnings from the girl, and thus she loathed the man whom her girl had fallen in love with. The very night she had taken the monk in as a guest, she was scheming to kill him.

"So she gave the lover some unwatered wine to make him lose his senses. He fell asleep, with the girl slumbering alongside him. When he was fast asleep, the woman went for the poison she has prepared. She placed it in a hollow reed so she could blow it into the man's 'nostrils,[Sp] putting one end of the reed into the man's 'nose[Sp] and the other in her own mouth.[7]

"All of a sudden, before she had a chance to blow in the reed, 'the man sneezed,℘) and the poison flew into the woman's throat so that she fell down dead.

"All that happened while the monk was looking on.

[D3. The Shoemaker's Wife]

"Then he arose in the morning and set off in search of the 'thief.℘ At another place,Y/CeD) a man who was a shoemaker took him in, saying to his wife. 'Take care of this monk; honor and lodge him fittingly, for some friends of mine have invited me to a party.'

"So the shoemaker went out.

"Now the shoemaker's wife was keeping company with a man, and their go-between was a woman who was married to a barber. So the shoemanker's wife sent a message telling the barber's wife to look for her sweetheart and inform him that her husband was with friends and would only come home drunk and late at night.

"At nightfall the man came right up to the door to wait for the woman, while the shoemaker came home after dark when he himself was drunk. When he saw the man standing at the door of his house, and he had already become suspicious of him, he got angry, went inside, and seized his wife. He beat her up terribly, and tied her feet to a post in the house.

"When all eyes were closed in slumber, the barber's wife came to her and said: 'Really, the man has been sitting at your doorstep for a long while! What do you think you should do?'

"The shoemaker's wife said: 'You see how I am;Y/CeD) but please be nice and kind to me: tie yourself in my place so I may go to my sweetheart.'

"The barber's wife did so.

"The shoemaker awoke before his wife's return and called her several times by name. The barber's wife did not answer for fear that he would recognize her voice. Then he called here and shouted her name several times, while the barber's wife never replied. His anger mounted, and he went up to her with his knife, cut off her nose, and said: 'Keep this and show it to your sweetheart!'

"When the shoemaker's wife came and found the barber's wife mutilated and her husband sleeping, she untied her and fastened herself in place. The other took her nose in her hand and went off home in a desperate condition. All that happened in the monk's sight and hearing.

"Then the shoemaker's wife raised her voice, calling upon her Lord and beseeching Him. She began to implore him, saying: "O God, if my husband has done me wrong, restore my nose in a sound state!'

"Her husband said to her: 'What's this you're saying, you witch!

"She said: "Get up, you evil-doer, and see what you have done, and how different God is from you! How merciful He is in view of my innocence of what you suspected me of! Indeed, God has restored my nose in a whole state!"

"So he got up, struck a light, and looked at his wife. He found her nose whole; so he confessed his sin to his Lord and apologized to his wife, begging her to think well of him

"As the barber's wife was trudging home, she was puzzling about some means of concealing herself. She said: 'What will be my excuse with my husband and family about my nose being cut off?'

"Now her husband awoke at dawn and called to her: 'Bring me my kit, for I want to go and bleed one of the town notables.'

"She didn't bring him any of his kit except the razor.

"So he repeated to her: "Bring me all my kit!'—but she still didn't bring him anything from his kit except his razor.

"The barber got angry and tossed the razor at her in the dark. She threw herself on the ground, and shrieked and howled and said: 'My nose! My nose!'

"She kept on until her people and close relatives came. They carried them both off to the judge, who said to the man: 'What induced you to cut off your wife's nose?'

"He had no argument forthcoming to save him, to the judge sentenced the barber to be punished.

"As they were taking him out to the scene of his punishment, the monk stood up and approached the judge. Then he said to him: 'You needn't be in any doubt, your worship, for the thief really did not steal from me, not the fox get killed by the goats, nor the whore by the poison, nor did the barber's wife get slashed by her husband—but we all did this by ourselves.

"The judge asked him to explain that, and he told him all about it."

Kalilah said to Dimnah: "And did you get into this scrape all by yourself, too?"

Dimnah said: "I have heard this fable indeed, and it is just like my case. Upon my life, no one has harmed me except myself; but how can I get out of it now?"

Kalilah said: "You give me your opinion about that."

Dimnah said: "So far as I'm concerned, I don't want anything better than to return to my former standing. But there are three necessities the intelligent man ought to attend to and 'contrive^n to get by all means. These are: attending to whatever advantage or disadvantage he receives; watching out lest the harm which struck him once should return again; and utilizing whatever may come his way that looks like an advantage and striving to secure it.

"Another of these lies in scrutinizing whatever advantage and profit from it, while not accepting the harm but bending his efforts towards getting rid of it. And still another is watching for an advantage in the future and whatever harm he may dread, and then working towards whatever he may be hoping for and guarding against whatever he may fear.

"So I have looked into the matter to see if there was any hope of returning to the rank which 'I once had$^{Y/CeD)}$ and he has now, and found no other means than plotting so the bull departs this life. That is the safest for me, since perhaps I'll thus be of some use to the lion, for he has overstepped himself in the bull's case, till it is an insult to his intelligence and is rousing the anger of the common people and of those close to him."

Kalilah said: "I don't see how the lion suffers any shame or harm in the bull's place with him nor the fine rank he has."

Dimnah said: "The fact is that the lion has taken such a great craze for the bull that he is overlooking all his old counsellors and is cutting himself off from them. Now it happens that a sovereign loses power because of six things; namely: awkwardness, privation, discord, passion, cruelty, and time.

"Privation is being deprived of the loyalty of one's retainers, counsellors, and politicians who have good judgment, courage, and fidelity, or alienating anyone like that. Discord tests men in accidents, strife, and battle. Passion means the craze for women, story-telling, drinking, hunting, and such like. Cruelty consists of a quick temper which often looses one's tongue in slander and one's hand in violence. As for time, it strikes men with evil, death, drowning, wasting the fruits of one's toil, and other similar things. Awkwardness means using violence in place of gentleness, and gentleness in place of violence."

Kalilah said: "How are you going to do anything with the bull when he is stronger than you and has more friends?"

Dimnah said: "Don't look at my smallness and weakness, for matters don't run just on strength and violence and weakness. Hasn't somebody who is small and weak already got the better of the lion? Or haven't you heard how the crow used her wits on a snake so that she killed it through her smoothness and insight?"

Kalilah said: "How was that?"

Dimnah said:

[E. The Crow and the Snake]

"Once upon a time a crow had her nest in a tree on a mountain close to a snake's lair. Each year when the crow was brooding, the snake used to go to her nest and eat her fledglings.

"When it had done this many times, and had got everything that it could out of the crow, the latter complained to a jackal friend of hers, saying: 'I'd like to consult you about something that is bothering me, so you can pass judgment on it and arrange something with me.'

"He said: 'What is it?'

"She said: 'I want to go to the snake and peck out its eyes.'

"The jackal said: 'What a mean trick you are thinking of pulling! Think up some means whereby you will come out ahead of the snake without getting killed yourself or risking your own life. Your story is like the story about the heron which wanted to kill the crayfish, but got killed himself instead.'

"The crow said: 'And how was that?'

"The jackal said:

[E1. The Heron and the Crayfish]

Once upon a time a heron wanted to kill a crayfish; his nest lay on the wooded bank of a river abounding in fish, where he had lived all his life. Then he grew too old and unfit for hunting, so that he got very hungry and tired. So he looked for some way out, and sat down in a sorrowful state.

Now he saw a crayfish approaching from a distance; and it said: "Why do I see you so ill and broken-hearted?"

The heron said: "Why can't I be as I was all my life up till now? I used to catch one or two fish every day from the fish that are here. I lived in that style, and the amount of fish never decreased.

"Now today I saw two fishermen going by, and one of them said to his companion: 'I see there are many fish here; let's fish for a while.'

"His companion said: 'I know of a spot ahead of us with lots of fish, and I'd like to begin there. Then when we have finished, we'll come back here and stay till we've finished with it.'

"Now I know that if they return, they will come back our way and not leave a single fish in this pool without catching it. So it will turn out, and that will be the death of me!"

The crayfish went off to all the other fish and informed them about that. They came to the heron for his advice, saying to him: "We have come to you for advice, so give us it: the intelligent person does not disregard his enemy's advice when he can judge the profit or harm of a matter. Now you are clever, and it is to your welfare and advantage that we keep on living; so give us your advice."

The heron said: "So far as killing or overwhelming the fishermen is concerned, I don't know of any way out except a spot with a pool of fresh water and reeds. If I could move you to that pool, it would be for your safety and welfare."

They said: "How can we move there unless you do it for us?"

He said: "I'll do that for you, but I'll go about it slowly lest the fishermen notice me before I have finished."

The heron did so. Each day he took a pair of fish, and carried them off to a hillside and ate them. He did not tell the rest of them about that, until one day the crayfish came to him saying: "I'm really worried about my position here, so take me to that pool!"

The heron carried the crayfish till he reached one of the places where he had been eating the fish. The crayfish looked down, and seeing many fishbones about, he realized that the heron was to blame and wanted to do the same with him as he had done with the other fish.

So the crayfish said to himself: "When a person chances upon an enemy in a region where he knows he is going to be killed whether he fights back or not, he should not meet [death] at his [enemy's] hands, except fighting for his honor and self-preservation."[8]

And the crayfish reached out with his pincers for the heron's neck and squeezed him so hard that he fell to the ground. The crayfish fell along with him. The heron died, and the crayfish cleared out and crawled back to the fish and told them about the affair.

"The jackal said to the crow: 'I have made this fable up so you will know how some tricks lead to the death of the trickster. However I'll show you something you can perform to bring about the snake's death and thus get rid of him.'

"The crow said: 'What is that?'

"He said: 'If you fly around and keep a sharp lookout, perhaps you will lay hold of some woman's piece of jewelry which is prized by her family. Snatch it away and then fly about the neighborhood until they catch sight of you. People will then go hunting you, so you may fly off to the snake's hole with the jewelry and throw it in on top of him. When the people go after their jewelry, they will catch the snake and give you peace from him.'

"So the crow went off till she found a woman putting on her clothes and jewelry in her room. While she was washing herself, she snatched a necklace from amongst her jewels and flew off with it. She continued flying about until people noticed her, so then she could go away to the snake's hole. She threw it in on top of him; so the people pounced upon the snake, killed it, and took the necklace."

Dimnah said to Kalilah: "I have made this fable up so you might know that a trick may 'suffice' where force will not."

Kalilah said: "Indeed the bull is just like that, since there is nothing smart about him even with all his strength. But along with his courage, he is a clever and intelligent person, and what can you do about that?"

Dimnah said: "The bull is exceedingly strong and clever, but I have fooled him and he trusts me. I'll be able to bowl him over just as the rabbit terrified the lion."

Kalilah said: "And how was that?"

Dimnah said:

[F. The Rabbit and the Lion]

"Once upon a time a lion lived in a well-watered and grassy country. Now that land had many wild animals because of the abundance of water and pasturage, but they didn't take advantage of it for fear of the lion. So these animals consulted together, assembled before the lion, and said to him:

'You never catch any of us by day except with toil and fatigue, while we see a way by which you and we will all get some rest. Provided you will trust and not fear us, we'll prepare an animal for you each day, which we'll send in time for your breakfast.'

"The lion consented to that and came to terms with them, while they all recognized his right to it.

"Then a rabbit was chosen in the drawing, and she said to them: 'If you will help me in something that won't hurt you, perhaps I may give you some peace from the lion!'

"They said: 'How do you want us to help you?'

"She said: 'Order whoever goes along with me not to follow closely, for I am going to loiter on my way to the lion so that his breakfast will be late.'

"They said: 'Have it your way.'

"So the rabbit ambled along until it was past the hour when the lion ate. She just crawled along at a snail's pace. The lion was hungry on account of the delay in his breakfast, and he was becoming angry. He stood up in his lair and walked about till, when he saw the rabbit, he said to her:

" 'Where are you coming from, and where is the animal?'

"She said: 'I am the animals' messenger; and they sent me along with a rabbit for you. When I was close, a lion met me and took it away, saying: "I am the leader in this land, and of its animals!"

" 'So I said to him: "This is the king's breakfast, and the animals sent me with it so that he does not become angry."

" 'He became annoyed and started insulting you, so I hurried to meet you and inform you about the matter.'

"So the lion got angry and said: 'Take me along and show me this lion!'

"She took the lion to a deep cistern full of clear water, and said: 'This is the lion's place. I am going away unless you carry me in your arms so I won't be afraid when I point him out to you!'

"The lion picked her up in his arms, and she brought him up to the clear water and said to him: 'Here are the lion and the rabbit.'

"He put the rabbit down and jumped in to kill the [lion] in the cistern; and the rabbit escaped."

Kalilah said: 'If you can bring about the bull's destruction without hurting the lion, that's your affair. The bull's position injures you and me and the lion's other attendants like us. Yet if you can't accomplish it without prejudicing the lion, don't try to buy yourself off in that way, for it will be treachery on both our parts, besides being a piece of villainy."

For several days Dimnah stopped paying court to the lion, and then he came to him when he was alone and sorrowful and at leisure.

The lion said to him: "How is it I haven't seen you since the day your spirits were depressed? In fact, I haven't seen you for days."

He said: "I wasn't hiding from you."

The lion said: "Good!"

He said: "May it be for the good."

The lion said: "Has something happened?"

Dimnah said: "Something has happened which neither the lion nor I would want."

The lion said: "What is that?"

Dimnah said: "It is a harsh and ugly thing which shouldn't be mentioned except in private."

The lion said: "But here we are solitary and alone, so tell me what's on your mind."

Dimnah said: "What there is to say will be disliked by whoever hears it, and he will not encourage its teller even though it is sound advice. Whoever says so is bold, unless the person he addresses is firm-minded. When the person addressed is intelligent, he will endure and heed it, since it is to the listener's advantage;

but so far as the teller is concerned, it is of no advantage to him except in doing what is right and advisable.

"But you, o king, are extremely observant and intelligent, and so I am going to risk telling what your majesty dislikes, since you know I am a sincere adviser and prefer your interests ahead of my own. I can't imagine how you are going to do anything but believe what I am telling you. However, when I recall that all of us beasts are dependent upon you, I find no other way than standing up for what is right, as I should, even if you do not ask me or I am afraid you will not accept it. For it is said: Whoever conceals sound advice from his sovereign, hides his illness from his physician, or covers up his poverty from his brethren, really deceives himself."

The lion said: "What is this matter?"

Dimnah said: "Someone whom I consider quite trustworthy informed me that Shatrabah got the heads of your army aside and said to them: 'I have tried the lion out and tested his understanding and strength and staunchness, and I am clearly impressed by how weak he is. There has already been an affair between him and me.'

"Now when this reached me, I knew that Shatrabah was a treacherous and unfaithful renegade, for you have loaded him down with all sorts of honors and made him a peer with yourself. Indeed, he has bent all his efforts towards reaching the same rank as you, and if you passed away, he would become our king, for he is always striving towards it. Indeed, it has been said: When a king knows that a man intends to become his equal in rank, judgment, appearance, wealth, and might, he may slay him; if he does not do so, he will be the one to get slain.

"You, o king, know things best and are most successful in them; while I see that you should do something about this matter before it gets out of hand. Don't wait for what is going to happen, for I don't know if you will be able to ward it off any longer or not. It has been said that there are three kinds of men: steady, shrewd, and weak.[9]

"The steady one is he who, when misfortune befalls him, is not bewildered nor loses his wits and understanding and shrewdness (which will all provide him with a way out), nor is his heart upset. The shrewd one is cleverer than the former, can view things from a distance, and knows what is going to happen ahead of time; he sees it all in its proper focus and contrives a way around it, since he has good foresight. He blocks a disease before it catches up on him, tossing an affair off before it happens. But the weakling is always behind times in his business, thinking he sees things clearly until they befall him, and by then he is so isolated and forlorn that he is lost. That story is the fable of the three fish."

The lion said: "How was that?"

Dimnah said:

[G. The Three Fish: Shrewd, Steady, and Weakling]

"Once upon a time there were three fish in a pool, and that pool lay in a stretch of land where no one approached. Now one day two fishermen were passing by, and they resolved to come back with their net and catch those three fish which they saw there.

"One fish was very shrewd, and she got suspicious and frightened; so she quickly took prompt action and left by the outlet where the water flowed from the pool into the river. Thus she changed over to a different spot.

"As for the other who was not quite so clever, she put off any action until the two fishermen came back, and then she said: 'Really I have been careless, and this is the result of it.'

"She saw them and knew what they wanted; and she found they had already blocked up the exit. So she said: 'I have been careless, and what can I contrive to get free in this case? A trick seldom succeeds in a hurry and after dallying; but let's not give the matter up nor stop looking for a way out.'

"Then as a stratagem, she played dead and floated upside down on the surface of the water. The fishermen picked her up, and reckoning she was dead, they placed her just where the river poured into the pool. She leaped into the river and slipped away from the fishermen.

"As for the weakling, she kept swimming back and forth until she was caught.

"And I advise your majesty to take energetic action against this piece of treachery, since you consider it the right way to look at it:

stop the disease before you catch it, and repel a nuisance before it befalls you."

The lion said: "I understand your story, but I don't think that the bull is hoodwinking me. He is not anxious for any mishap to befall me after my pleasant dealings with him and what I have done for him. He cannot mention a single ugly thing I have done him nor any kindness I have not thrown his way."

Dimnah said: "Hasn't your intelligence gone bad on you? The favors you have shown him have led him to covet your rank for himself. The baseborn weakling is always sincere and useful until he reaches an office he is unworthy of. When he has achieved this, he covets something else and aspires to climb higher through fraud and treachery. The lowly renegade does not serve his sovereign nor advise him except through fear or necessity; when he is rich and confident, he returns to his nature and origin, like the dog's bent tail which is tied to make it stand straight up, and can be kept so just as long as it is tied; but once it is released, it becomes curled and twisted again.

"Know, o king, that 'whoever$^{\mathfrak{P}}$' does not accept what may vex him from his counsellors when they are advising him, does not deserve the fruit of their judgment. He is like a sick man who lays aside what the doctors prescribe for him and follows his own selfish desires. A sovereign's minister ought to 'strive to rouse$^{\eta}$' him to what 'will increase his monarch's power$^{\eta}$', and urge him away from what will injure and harm him. The best of women is she who adapts herself 'to her$^{\eta}$' 'husband$^{Y/CeD)}$'. The best praise is what is in the mouths of the best people. 'The finest king is the one who does not become insolent nor feel he is too big to receive advice$^{\eta}$'. The best friend is one who is not quarrelsome. The paragon of the rich is he who is not a captive of greed. 'And the best character is that which tends to godliness$^{\eta}$'."

Then he added: "If a man uses snakes as a pillow and stretches out on fire, he is more apt to indulge in sleep than if he sees his friend holds a grudge against him while he must live with him day and night. The weakest of kings is easy-going with them and lax in tending to matters; he is like the rutting elephant which does not heed a thing and scorns whatever is told him."

The lion said: "These are harsh words you say, but the words of a sincere counsellor should be accepted even if they make things difficult. Yet if Shatrabah is an enemy as you say, he cannot harm me. How could he? He eats grass and I eat flesh; so he is food for me. I don't see anything to fear from him nor any way for him to be treacherous after the trust I have placed in him and the inviolability of his confidence in me, and how I have honored and praised him amongst all my followers. If I were to do that, I would be showing up my own ignorance and betraying my responsibility."

Dimnah said: "You were not fooling yourself with your words: 'He is food for me', for if the bull cannot overpower you himself, he will get the better of you through some one else. It has been said: If a guest lodges with you for one hour, be on your guard if you do not know his disposition. Don't trust yourself, lest some evil strike you from or because of him, just as the louse was injured when she played host to the flea."

The lion said: "What befell the louse?"

Dimnah said:

[H. The Hospitable Louse and the Flea]

"Once upon a time a louse had taken up quarters in a certain nobleman's bed. She drank his blood while he was sleeping, for she crawled over him very gently.

"One night a flea asked her to lodge him in that nobleman's bed. ⌈She took him in, saying: 'Stay with me tonight and have some delicious blood and a soft bed!'

"The flea did so and lodged with her. When the man went to bed⌉, he bit him so hard that he awoke; so the man ⌈got up and⌉ ordered ⌈the sheet shaken⌉ to see ⌈if there was anything in⌉ in his bed.

"The flea jumped out and escaped, while the louse ⌈which could not walk so well⌉ was caught and crushed to death.

"I have only made this story up for you in order to explain how there is no safety from the evil of a bad man. If one is lax for his sake, calamity strikes just because of it. Now if you don't fear the bull, beware of some one else in your entourage whom he has already filled with enmity and incited against you. For I know for certain that there is no way except by seeing it out with you, nor will he allow anyone but himself to handle the matter."

The lion was sorry at Dimnah's speech, and he said to him: "What do you suggest I do?"

Dimnah said: "A person with a broken, rotten molar does not let it keep on bothering him, for it hurts till he gets rid of it. If food has gone bad, he gets relief only by throwing it away. The cure for an enemy you fear lies in doing away with him."

The lion said: "You have made me dislike having any more dealings with Shatrabah. I'm sending for him to tell him how hurt I am!"

Then he ordered him to leave. Dimnah became pensive and realized that if the lion were to talk to the bull and hear his vindication, he would know that Dimnah had been lying and so he could not keep the matter concealed.

Dimnah said to the lion: "I don't approve of sending for the bull and telling him about his faults. Observe this point, your majesty, that your affairs will keep on for the best so long as you do not disclose what is on your mind. I am afraid that if you reveal it to him, he will hasten to come to blows, and if he fights you, he will fight well-prepared; while if he forsakes you, he will get the better of you because of his treachery. Besides, resolute kings should not reveal a man's punishment to one who does not reveal his crime, but every crime has its own punishment. The crime of secrecy is punished in secret, while an open crime should be punished openly."

The lion said: "When a king punishes some one or disgraces him on mere conjecture and without clear evidence as to his guilt, he only punishes and disgraces himself."

Dimnah said: "Don't let him in to see you except when you are ready, nor let him get you off guard! I reckon that if you watch him when he comes to you, you are going to notice that he has something important on his mind. One of the signs is that you will see his color change, his limbs tremble, and he will turn right or left, setting his horns like some one who is preparing to gore."

The lion said, "I'll be on my guard against him. Thus I'll see any of these signs you mention concerning his doubtful conduct."

When Dimnah had finished with the lion, he knew that he had dropped what he wanted in his mind, and that the lion would beware of the bull and take measures against him. He then wanted to go to the bull and 'incite him against $^{Y/CeD)}$ the lion. He preferred to be sent at the lion's behest lest anybody else inform him and lead the bull to suspect him.

So he said to the lion: "What about my going to the bull and keeping a watch on him? I'll see what state he is in and hear what he says, and maybe I'll learn something about what he is doing."

The lion agreed to that.

So Dimnah went off and entered the bull's quarters as if his heart were broken. When the bull saw him, he welcomed him and said? "I haven't seen you for days; what has kept you away? Have you been ill?"

Dimnah said: "When can anyone be easy if he has no control over himself? Or if his business is being handled by some one he does not trust who is constantly terrorizing him and endangering his life, so that not an hour passes but he is in fear of his person and of his blood being shed?"

The bull said: "What has happened?"

Dimnah said: "What was fated, happened; and who can overcome fate? Whoever achieves success gets fat, and can't 'move fast' nor is he grateful. Who follows his passions and is not worn out? Who keeps company with women and doesn't get deceived? Who tries to get things out of people and is not despised? Who carries on evil habits and comes out whole? And who has a sovereign's friendship and is not left in the lurch? Indeed, the fellow who said the following hit it right: A sovereign resembles a steady-going harlot who, when one chap leaves, another comes along; for he is faithless towards his friends and 'ungenerous' towards those who ruin themselves for him."

Shatrabah said: "I have heard what you have to say, and fear it may be that there is some reason to suspect the lion."

Dimnah said: "I am rather suspicious of him, but not on my own account. You know your ties to me well enough, and the attachment there is between us, and what I did for you of my own accord, and my pledge the time the lion sent me to you. Now I don't find any way out of your ties except by telling you how I fear for you."

Shatrabah said: "How so?"

Dimnah said: "Some one honest and trustworthy informed me that the lion told some of his intimates and friends: 'I am astonished at how fat the bull is getting. Since I haven't any need for him nor see anything but eating him, let's have a feast off his flesh!'

"When I heard about this speech of his, I realized how faithless and bad his word was, and I am passing it along to you so you may know it. Thus I am fulfilling what I owe you, so that you can find some way of handling this matter."

When Shatrabah heard what Dimnah had to say, he remembered Dimnah's oath and promise to him. He thought about the lion, believing that Dimnah had really told him the truth and advised him well.

Shatrabah said to Dimnah:[10] "It is not proper for the lion to deceive me, since I have never offended him nor any of his retainers. I have been charged falsely and he has been made suspicious. The lion keeps company with evil people and 'lies occur[n]' on their part. They get him to believe them 'more than[Sp]' what he hears elsewhere. Similarly, evil men's companionship may occasion much lasting grief and bad thoughts about better men, so that this experience leads one to go astray like the duck.

[I. The Duck and the Star][11]

"A duck once saw the glimmer of a star in the water. She thought it was a fish and sought to catch it. When she had tried that several times, she knew it wasn't anything.

"So another night when she was looking at the bottom of the pool, she did see a fish in the same place. She thought it was the same as before, and didn't fish for it nor try to catch it.

"So if the lion has learned anything about me and believed it, preferring to find out from some one besides myself, it 'is on purpose[Sp]'. If he has been harmed by me and wishes me evil without reason, then that is strange. For it has been said that one rarely seeks to please one's companion or to desire his pleasure and not be pleased himself.

"The strangest part is that he seems quite happy, and then he becomes discontented. When discontent has no excuse, it is hopeless, for if an outburst has a motive for coming to a head, it has thereby a means of calming down again, since it loses its meaning and vanity once it has nowhere to settle.

"I have been reflecting, and I don't know what trouble is keeping the lion and me apart, unless it is petty. Upon my life, no one could keep up a friendship if he had to watch every single detail and take care lest the smallest or biggest word should slip out which his friend would disapprove of. When a friend makes a slip or commits some offence, the sensible and steadfast person only notices the result of the slip or offence, and whether it were deliberate or only a slip, and if by forgiving him he need fear any harm or disgrace. Then he never takes his friend to task when he finds a way of forgiving him.

"If the lion has found fault with me, I don't know about it unless perhaps I disagreed with him on some decision, from my own point of view and purely as a matter of advice. Maybe I brought this upon myself through being bold and disagreeing with him when he said 'No' and I said 'Yes,' and he said 'Yes' and I said 'No.' But I don't attribute it to having said this, since I haven't disagreed with him about anything at all concerning the heads of his army, except when I was considering his profit and advantage.

"Nor have I said any of this in front of the heads of his army or his leaders and companions; but I took him aside and tried what I could by discussing it with him in the tone of a man loyal to his lord and with confidence in him. I know that whoever looks for humbleness in his advisers during consultation, in his physicians during treatment, and in his lawyers in a doubtful case, spoils the usefulness of their judgment, aggravates his illness, and commits a fault against tradition.

"Now if it weren't this, maybe it was during one of our sovereign's tipsy moods. Sometimes when he's drunk, he prefers some one he should be angry with, and gets angry with some one who should be preferred, and for no apparent reason. Thus wise men say: He who goes down to the sea in ships risks his life, and still more a sovereign's companion; for even if he is a steadfast friend, upright, affectionate, and sincere, he will probably stumble and not get up again, or if he makes a comeback, he risks his life by doing so.

"If it isn't this, perhaps my good conduct towards him has been my downfall. A fine tree may be ruined by yielding splendid fruit, when its branches bear so well that they are dragged down to be broken and spoiled. The peacock may find its tail beautiful and handsome when it is raised, while 'when⁽ˢᵖ⁾ it tries to be nimble and swift, fleeing from some one who wants to catch it, its tail holds it back. The fleet and mighty steed may meet its death by being worried and tired and made to toil with all its superiority until it loses its life. The outstanding man may meet his death in the wicked folk who envy and hold a grudge against him; for there are more bad people everywhere than good folk, and when they hate him and are more numerous, they are quick to put him out of the way.

"And if it isn't this, then it may be fate which is never averted, for fate deprives the lion of his strength and power until he is fit to be buried. It carries the weakling on the elephant's back and gives the charmer mastery over the snake so that he can pull its fangs out and play with it as he likes. It is what makes the energetic man weak and energizes the weakling, dulls the sharpster and sharpens the dullard, makes things easy for the chap who is hard up and hard for the chap who is well off, and heartens the coward and disheartens the courageous. Predetermined factors may be distinguished from the confused causes which can give one an advantage over his competitors."

Dimnah said: "Whatever the lion may be wishing, it is not in the least because evil-doers are urging him on as you mention nor anything like that, but because of his own treachery and lax character. He is proud and treacherous, and starts by feeding you sweets and later on bitters, or even more deadly poison that kills."

Shatrabah said: "You have spoken the truth, upon my life! I have been fed 'sweets'ⁿ and enjoyed myself, while I see I have come close to death. What is it except fate that has brought me to stay with the lion? He eats flesh while I eat grass. Unnatural greed and ugly hope have tossed me into this abyss and now are keeping me from escaping, as the bee is held on a waterlily: when she catches its scent and is enjoying it, she forgets her instinct which urges her to fly away before the waterlily closes 'at nightfall'ⁿ and squeezes her to death inside.

"He who is not content with this world's goods, letting his soul strain after excellence and abundance ant not seeing what there is to fear ahead of him, is like the fly which is not satisfied with trees and shrubs, but seeks the moisture dripping from the rutting ele-

phant, so that the pachyderm switches its ear and kills it. Whoever
bestows his advice and energy upon an ingrate is like one who
sows a saltmarsh ar advises the dead."

Dimnah said: "Stop talking like that and try to do something
for yourself!"

Shatrabah said: "Is there anything I can do for myself if the lion
wants to kill me? I know the lion's character and how he looks at
things. Even if he wants to do only the best by me, while his companions want to kill me by hook or by crook right under his nose,
they will manage it. For if craft and injustice club together against
the innocent and upright man, they are capable of destroying him,
even if they are weak and he is strong; just as the wolf, the crow,
and the jackal destroyed the camel the time they connived to coax
and wheedle him."

Dimnah said: "How was that?"

The bull said:

[J. The Innocent Camel][12]

"Once upon a time a lion lived in a thicket near a road where
men used to pass. He had three companions: a wolf, a jackal, and a
crow. Now some merchants passed along that road, and a camel of
theirs remained behind them. He went into a thicket till he met
the lion.

"The lion said to him: 'Where are you from?'

"So he informed him about his business.

"'The lion[9] said: 'What do you want?'

"He replied: 'I want to be friends with the king.'

"He said: 'If you want my friendship, then keep company with
me in confidence, having plenty to eat and an easy life.'

"So the camel stayed on with the lion until one day the lion
went off in search of game. He met an elephant and killed it in a
tremendous fight. The lion came away with blood flowing from
the wounds which the elephant had inflicted upon him with its
tusks, and felt so mangled that he couldn't hunt anymore.

"The wolf, the jackal, and the crow hung around for some days
without turning up a thing from the lion's leavings which they
could live off. Hunger smote them and they became exceedingly

lean. The lion realized this and said: 'Strive and contrive to get something to eat!'

"They said. 'We aren't worried about ourselves while we see the state the king is in, and we can't find anything to help your majesty get well.'

"The lion said: 'I don't doubt your affection and friendship; but if you can, spread out in such a way that you may run across some game and bring it to me. Maybe something good for you and myself will turn up.'

"So the wolf, the crow, and the jackal left the lion's presence and went off nearby to consult together. They said: 'What good is this camel that only eats grass? His business does not concern us nor does he see things our way. Why don't we dress him up so the lion can eat him and we can feed off his flesh?'

"The jackal said: 'You dare not mention this to the lion, for he pledged the camel and made a compact with him.'

"The crow said: 'You stay where you are and leave the lion to me.'

"So the crow went off to the lion, and when he caught sight of him, the lion said to him: "Have you come across anything?'

"The crow said to him: 'Whoever isn't zealous doesn't find, who hasn't perception doesn't see, and perception and sight have both fled from us ever since we became hungry. However, we have looked into something and agreed upon it; so if you agree with us, then we shall be in clover.'

"The lion said: 'What is it?'

"The crow said: "This grass-eating camel is luxuriating in our midst beyond all profit.'

"The lion got angry at this and said: 'Curses upon you for the way you talk nonsense and how your insight has failed you! How disloyal and unmerciful you are! You aren't fit to approach me and talk this way. Don't you know I pledged the camel and granted him protection? Hasn't it ever reached your ears that when an almsgiver gives alms, 'it is a greater boon than if he protects some fearful soul$^{Y/CeD)}$ or prevents bloodshed? Now I granted the camel protection, and I was not acting treacherously in doing so!'

"The crow said: I know what the king is saying; but a single soul can redeem a household, a household can redeem a tribe, a tribe can redeem a country, and a country redeems a king when need overwhelms him.[13] I can find a way for your majesty to get out of his pledge. The lion does not need to pretend that he is being treacherous himself, nor giving any orders about it; but we shall contrive some scheme whereby the king may remain loyal to his oath and we may still get what we need.'

"The lion was silent, so the crow went off to his companions and said: 'I have talked the lion into giving me a free hand in those matters. What trick is there for [dealing with] the camel, since the lion refuses to take charge of killing him or to order it?'

"Both his companions said: 'We expect you to help and advise us in this matter.'[14]

"The crow said: 'My advice is for us to get together with the camel and mention the lion's condition, and how hungry and distraught he has become. Let's say: "He has been very kind to us and shown us much consideration. If he does not experience some good for us today, and notice how concerned we are for his lot and that we are anxious about his health, that will show we have mean dispositions and are ungrateful for his favors. Rather let's go along to the lion and mention the kindness we have experienced from him, how we have lived under his aegis, and how he needs our gratitude and loyalty. If we are to be of any service to him, then we should grant him it without reserve; while if we cannot do that, he has our persons as a free gift."

" 'Then let each one of us present himself and say: "Eat me, your majesty, and don't die of hunger!" When one person says that, another will answer, contradicting him with some excuse or other, and he will be saved. Thus we will all save ourselves, and still justify the king's pledge.'

"So they did that, and the camel fell in with the idea. They approached the king, and the crow started in by saying: 'Your majesty, you need something to sustain you. We should be of some use to you ourselves, for we have been living through you, and so will any offspring who come after us. If you perished, we would not have any posterity left nor any object in living. Now I would like you to eat me so that I may benefit you.'

"But the wolf, the camel, and the jackel answered him: 'Keep quiet! What are you, and how is there enough for the king if he eats you?'

"The jackal said: "I'd be enough for the king!'

"The wolf, the camel, and the crow said: 'You stink in your guts, and your breath smells like tainted meat. We're afraid that if the king ate you, your filthy flesh would kill him!'

"The wolf said: 'But I'm not at all like that, so the king may eat me.'

"The crow, the jackal, and the camel said: 'Whoever wants to commit suicide will eat wolf meat. He'll catch hoof-and-mouth disease from it!'

"Now the camel thought that when he said the same thing, they would find a way out for him as they had for themselves, and he would be safe and the lion pleased. The camel said: 'But, your majesty, my flesh is good and wholesome, and the king can get enough of it.'

"The wolf, the crow, and the jackal all said: 'You are right! How generous you are in saying just what we knew all along!'

"So they pounced upon him and tore him to pieces.

"Now I have made this fable up for the lion and his companions since I know that if they agree upon my death, I cannot prevent them, even if the lion's opinion is different and he has nothing but good in his heart. Indeed it is said that the best monarch is like a vulture hovering around carcasses, not like carcasses with vultures around them. And even if the lion has only mercy and love in his soul, ⸢all this talking will alter that, for when there is a lot of it, it will not stop until compassion and mercy are driven away.⸣

"Don't you see that water is softer than the voice, and stone is stronger than the heart? Does not water finally leave a mark upon a hard stone after dripping on it for a long while? ⸢How much more the soft hearts of men by clever persons who attack them with slander!⸣"

Dimnah said: "Now what do you want to do?"

Shatrabah said: "I don't see anything but fighting him, for the praying man at his prayer, the almsgiver in his alms, and the godly man through his piety, never obtain the reward of the man who fights for one hour of the day when his struggle is in the right; for he is struggling in his self-defence. His reward is great and his fame is exalted, whether he vanquishes or is vanquished."

Dimnah said: "I don't see it this way: ⸢one shouldn't risk his life when he can do something else; the man of insight uses killing as a last resort, starting out as gently and shrewdly as he can,⸣ because if he dies, he loses his soul and thereby sins, and if he wins it is fate.[SP] Indeed it has been said: Don't think lightly of an enemy, no matter how mean and weak and cringing he may seem, especially when he is crafty and can rely upon helpers. How can you handle the lion with his daring and might? He who despises the weakling for his weakness will be struck by what the sandpipers used to smite the Old Man of the Sea."

Shatrabah said: "How was that?"

Dimnah said:

[K. The Old Man of the Sea and the Sandpipers][15]

"Once upon a time a sea bird called the Titiway had his home on one of the shores of the sea along with his mate. When it came time for them to brood, the female said to the male:

" 'The time has come for me to lay my eggs, so find an out-of-the-way spot for me to lay them in.'

"The male said: 'Why not let it be this spot where we are now? We have water and grass close by, and are near everything we want. It is very handy for us indeed.'

"The female said: 'Better watch what you are saying, for I am in danger in this place of ours! If the sea should rise, it will carry off our chicks.'

"The male said: 'I don't think the sea will act so foolishly towards us. What is there to fear from the Old Man of the Sea in the way of boldness?'

"The female said: 'How headstrong you are in saying this! You ought to be ashamed of threatening the Old Man of the Sea and rebelling against him. You yourself know, and it is true, that nothing knows less about itself than man. So hear what I have to say and help move us out of this spot before something happens to us that we won't like.'

"The male refused to agree with her, and when she kept on pleading more and more, he would not even listen to her.

"She said: 'Whoever does not listen to his companions and friends will have happen to him what happened to the turtle when it did not accept its companions' words.'

"The male said[SP]: 'How does this story go?'

"The female said:

[K.1 The Talkative Turtle]¹⁶

Once upon a time two ducks and a turtle lived together in a fountain. They had struck up an acquaintance due to their intimacy. Then the water in that spring began to go down at a fearful rate.

When the two ducks saw how the water was going down, they said: "We'd better leave this spring and move elsewhere!"

So they took their leave of the turtle and said: "Good-bye, for we're going away."

The turtle said: "It is terrible the way this water is going down for the like of a poor soul like me who can't get a living except in the water. You two can live wherever you may choose to go; so can't you think of some means to take me along?"

They said: "We won't be able to take you with us unless you agree that when we fly with you in the air and people see and call out to you, you won't answer them."

It did so and agreed not to answer anyone. 'It said: "I'll do so;⁹⁾ except how are you going to carry me?"

They said: "Bite the middle of a stick, and we'll take hold of both ends and lift it up into the air."

It was pleased at that, and they carried it up high. When people saw it, they shouted and said: "Look at the wonderful sight of a turtle between two ducks in the air."

When the turtle heard what they were saying and how astonished they were, it said: "May God tear your eyes out!"

When it opened its mouth to speak, it fell to the earth and was killed.

"The sandpiper said: 'I have heard what you have to say, but don't be afraid of the sea.'

"So the female hatched her chicks where she was. When the Old Man of the Sea heard the male sandpiper's voice, the sea rose and carried off the nest with its chicks, and they disappeared.

"So when the female lost her chicks, she said to the male: 'I knew right from the start that things were going to be like this for us, and all your lack of self-knowledge would come back upon us. Look what kind of misfortune has struck us!'

"The male sandpiper said: 'What I said when this business started, I say now when it is all over: if the sea has acted so foolishly towards us, it will soon see what I'll do about it.'

"He put on a bold front, and went off to his companions. He complained to them about what he had suffered from the Old Man of the Sea and what had happened to him, saying: 'You are my brethren and family, and my hope in seeking redress for my injury. Help me find some way out, because perhaps what happened to me today will befall you tomorrow.'

"They said: 'We are your helpers in this insofar as we can; but what is there 'we⁽ᴾ⁾' might be able to do against the sea?'

"The sandpiper said: 'Assemble so we may go to our colleagues the birds and complain to them about how we were molested by the sea, and how it has injured us. Let's say: "You are birds like us, so aid us lest what befell us today befalls you tomorrow." '

"So the male sandpiper gathered all the birds together in one spot and complained to them about what had happened.

"The birds said: 'We are at your service, but what can we do against the sea?'

"The sandpiper said: 'O assembly of birds, our liege-lady is 'Garuda⁽ᴾ⁾', the griffin-eagle. Let us beseech her constantly and call upon her at the top of our voices till she intercedes for us with the Old Man of the Sea.'

"The griffin answered them and appeared on the scene. She said: 'What has brought you together, and why are you calling on me?'

"They complained to her about what they had suffered from the Old Man of the Sea, saying: 'You are our patron, and 'Visnu⁽ᴾ⁾' the king who rides you is more powerful than the Sea Sprite. Please go and look for him.'

"The griffin did so, and 'Visnu⁽ᴾ⁾' who bestrides her went off towards the Old Man of the Sea to kill him. When the Old Man of the Sea realized his weakness when faced with the power of that king who rides the griffin, he was quick to return the chicks.

"Now I have told you this tale to let you know that one needn't risk his life if he can avoid it; for if he is killed, it is said that he lost his life, and if he outlives the fight, it is fate. But the intelligent man hastens to fight, and turns his back upon trickery, provided he has already tried as hard as he can to be gentle and shrewd."

The bull said: "I am not the lion's opponent, nor am I going to show him enmity in secret or openly. Neither will I treat him any different until he makes it clear that I must fear for my life."

Dimnah said, (for he disliked his statement 'Neither will I treat him any different', and thought that the lion, if he did not see the signs he had mentioned in the bull, would suspect him and tell the bull so): "Now if you watch the lion, what you want to see will be quite apparent."

The bull said: "How will I know that?"

Dimnah said: "If you will observe the lion as he is watching you, he will be getting up and squatting down, heaving his breast mightily, keeping his glance fixed upon you, bristling his ears, his mouth gaping, and drumming the earth with his tail. Thus you will know that he wants to kill you."

The bull said: "If I see any of these signs, there won't be any more doubt about it."

When Dimnah had finished inciting the lion against Shatrabah, and Shatrabah against the lion, he went off to Kalilah. When he reached him, Kalilah said to him: "How far did you get in your business?"

Dimnah said: "I have almost attained my objective and yours. Don't doubt or think that two friends' affection can be maintained when a cunning and smooth person contrives to break it up."

Then Kalilah and Dimnah went off together to meet the lion, and they met Shatrabah entering his presence. When the lion saw him, he rose from his haunches, pricked up his ears, opened his mouth, and beat the earth with his tail.

The bull was sure he was going to spring upon him, and he said to himself: "How little faith has a sovereign's friend in him, and how he dreads lest his temper get on edge so he will change his mind because of the covetousness, slander, and lying he hears! Is he not like the owner of a viper which he keeps by him at night, and doesn't know what is pricking him? Or like living next to a lion in his den; or swimming in water infested with crocodiles which may attack him at any moment?"

The bull kept thinking about this while he was preparing to fight the lion if the latter wanted it.

When the lion noticed how frightened the former was, and how he was coming into his presence with evil thoughts, he saw some of the signs that Dimnah had mentioned to him. The lion did not doubt but that he was coming to kill him, so he sprang upon him and they both got tangled up in the fray. The bull struggled so hard that it lasted a long time, and blood gushed from them both.

When Kalilah saw what had happened to the lion and the blood flowing, he said to Dimnah: "Look at what you've brought about! What a nasty business it is, and how badly it has ended!"

'Dimnah said: "How so?"

Kalilah said: "The lion is wounded and the bull has perished."[n]

Then Kalilah said, for the lion cried out when he saw that the bull had died, that the court was a-talking, and how criticism was taking different turns: "Now they clearly see your blundering, which you insisted was such a smooth way of handling things. Don't you know that the clumsiest blunderer is he who insists upon fighting his friend when he can get out of it? Doesn't a man often get his opportunity to fight and drop it, fearing to expose himself to danger and disgrace, and hoping he may be able to prevail upon his companion through some other sort of struggle?

"When a sovereign's minister tells him to wage open conflict while he can win his way through conciliation and thus gain his point, he shows he is a worse enemy than his tongue. Just as palsy overcomes the tongue when one's mind is feeble, likewise paralysis overcomes valor when one errs in judgment: for whoever lacks either valor or judgment, has no store of the other in any conflict, for many matters are accomplished through judgment without daring, but daring accomplishes nothing by dispensing with judgment. Whoever wants to be wily and does not know what course of judgment will bring him to it, does things the way you have done them.[17]

"Now I knew about your greed and conceited opinion, and I always dreaded the scabby action you were bringing down upon me and yourself, as soon as I saw and heard what you had to say. For the intelligent man begins by looking into matters and consequences before sticking his finger into them; and where he can hope to attain his desire, he advances upon it, and where he fears not to achieve it, he goes off and leaves it alone. Nothing prevented me from scolding you at the start of your adventure and stopping you from committing this offence, except it was a matter one dared not disclose, and I needed witnesses and helpers against you; for I knew that my word would neither help you nor deter you from evil.

"But now since your vile judgment and bungling are obvious, and I see the evil consequences of your action, I am going to tell you all about yourself and your vices. One of these is that you are pleasant in your talk, and wicked in your actions. Indeed, it is said: There is nothing more harmful to a monarch than an associate who is a fine talker but who doesn't act well. You just fooled the lion because you have such a nice manner of speaking, and now you have ruined him since you haven't such a fine way of acting.

"There is no good in talking without action, in seeing without experience, in wealth without generosity, in a friend without loyalty, in self-restraint without godliness, in truthfulness without good intentions, nor in living except in health, safety, and happiness. You have ⸢wrought⸣ a thing that only the clever and gentle man can cure, just like the sick man who combines symptoms of various diseases and illnesses which no one can treat except the skilled physician.

"Now know that ⸢learning, the destroyer of arrogance, begets arrogance in fools⸣, just as daylight ⸢increases⸣ the vision of any sighted creature while bats have worse sight. The intelligent person is not made vain by the rank which befalls him nor the honor which he has achieved, just as the mountain does not tremble no matter how violent the wind may be. Similarly, the ninny becomes cocksure with the humblest rank, like grass which moves in the slightest breeze.

"I have just now remembered something I heard mentioned about a sovereign, that when he is honest while his ministers are bad and withhold his benefits from the people, then no one can profit from his benefits nor his good works. That is exactly like good, clear water where there are crocodiles; no one can go in even if he is a swimmer and needs to. The deceit of kings and their adornment are their intimates, depending upon whether there are many of them who are honest or not.

"Now you don't want the lion to deal with any business without you, whereas a monarch is towards his associates only as the sea is with its waves.[18] It is stupidity for a man to seek brethren without being loyal, the ⸢other world⸣[Y/CeD] through hypocrisy, the love of women through being crude, ⸢one's own advantage through

harming another[Y/CeD], and knowledge and prestige through idling
and learning 'nothing[Sp]'.

"But what's the use of talking this way, and what does this
preaching accomplish? I know that this matter is just as the man
said to the bird: 'Don't try to set something right which cannot be
set right, nor admonish what doesn't heed you.' "

Dimnah said: "How was that?"

Kalilah said:

[L. The Apes, the Firefly, and the Bird]

"Once upon a time, a band of apes lived on a certain mountain. One 'cold[Y/CeD]' night they noticed a firefly flying around, and
they thought it was a spark; so they gathered some firewood and
place it upon it. Then they began blowing [on the fire].

"Now near them was a tree where there was a bird. It started
calling to them that what they saw was not fire; but they refused
to listen to it. So it flew down to show them.

"A man who was passing by said: 'O bird, don't try to set
something right which is impossible, nor to teach something that
cannot be taught! It is a waste of effort to bother with what can't
be straightened out, and only ends in regret. A stone that cannot
be cut, cannot be marked by swords; and there is no use in striving to bend a stick that cannot be bent. Whoever sets to work on
what can't be straightened out, only regrets it.'

"But the bird refused to listen to that man, or to profit from
anything he said. He went closer to the apes to make them
understand how the firefly wasn't fire. Thus one of the apes
reached out and ripped off its head.

"Now this story suits you since you don't want to take advantage of admonishment and warning. Really, Dimnah, cunning
and weak character have got the better of you, and they are two
bad friends, cunning being the worse in its consequences. They
can both be compared to the wily man who was the dupe's
companion."

Dimnah said: "How was that?"

Kalilah said:

[M. The Rogue and the Dupe]

"Once upon a time, a rogue and a dupe were partners in business. On the road they chanced upon a purse containing a thousand dinars. They both had to return home, and as they were approaching their town, they sat down to divide the dinars.

"So the dupe said to the rogue: 'You take half, and give me half.'

"Meanwhile the rogue had been thinking of some means to get away with all of it; so he said: 'Let's not divide it, for sharing and having in common is closer to honesty and sincerity. Let's bury the remainder in a safe place so that when we need expense money, we can both come and take what we need.'

"The dupe said: 'Yes.'

"So they took a trifling sum from the dinars, and buried the rest at the foot of a large tree of the tallest sort. Then the rogue reneged about the dinars and took them, patting the earth back into place.

"Some months later, the dupe said to the rogue: 'We need some expense money, so let's go off and take our expenses out of the dinars.'

"So they both went off to the tree. They dug up where the dinars had been, and didn't find a thing.

"The rogue grabbed his hair and pulled it out, beating his breast and shouting: 'Nobody can trust anyone! Even one's brother and friend will deceive you! You came back and took the dinars!'

"The dupe began to deny it and swear up and down, while the rogue kept on till he became violent and said to him: 'Who'd take it besides you? Would anyone other than us get wind of it?'

"Then the rogue took hold of the dupe and went off to the judge with him. He told him the whole story, and insisted that the dupe had taken the dinars.

"So the judge said to him: 'Have you any proof about this?'

"The rogue said: 'Yes, the tree at whose roots the dinars lay, will bear witness for me.'

"The judge was surprised at his claim that the tree would bear him witness, and reproached him for what he had said, ordering him to get bail for himself. And he said to the bondholder: 'Be sure to bring him along tomorrow so that what he claims about the tree bearing witness can be straightened out.'

"The rogue went off home and told his father the story, saying: 'Father, I only asked witness of the tree because of something that occurred to me, and I'm relying on you to bear out what I claim. If you want, we can keep the dinars, and earn as much again from the dupe.'

"The rogue's father said: 'What are you ordering me to do?'

"The rogue said: 'I purposely chose the largest sort of tree in existence for the dinars. It has a hollow trunk you can get into without being seen, and I buried them at its foot. Then I went back, took them, and accused the dupe. Now I want you to go off at night and get in there. When the judge comes and asks the tree for its testimony, you will speak from inside and say: "The dupe took the dinars!" '

"The rascal's father said: 'Son, a trick may catch the trickster; you're planning something like the duck plotted.'

"The scoundrel said: 'How was that, father?'

"The rascal's father said:

[M.1 The Smart Duck]

Once upon a time a duck lived near a snake, and whenever the duck had any ducklings, the snake would come to her nest and eat her young. Now the duck was well-fixed there and unable to leave, and she was saddened by what the snake was doing to her. A crab found out about that, and came to say: "What makes you so sad?"

So she told him what was happening.

The crab said to her: "Do you want me to show you something to help you get rid of the snake?"

She said: "What is that?"

The crab took her to a cavern across the way and said: "Do you see this cave? Now here lives a weasel who hates snakes; so gather a lot of fish and then place pieces all the way from the snake's hole to the weasel's. The weasel will eat the first fish, and the next, until he comes to the snake's hole and kills it."

The duck did that, and the weasel came up to the snake and killed it. Then he went back, sniffing along as usual, till he chanced upon the duck's nest, since it was so close to the other. So he ate the duck and her ducklings.

"Now I have made this story up to teach you that whoever is not sure about what trick he is playing, finds that it comes back upon him worse than he played it on some one else.'

"The rogue said: 'I have heard this story, but don't be so frightened, for the matter is easier than you think.'

"So the old man gave in to his son, followed him to the tree, and climbed inside. Next morning the judge, the rogue, and the dupe arrived at the tree, and the judge asked it: 'Have you any evidence?'

"The old man answered form inside the tree: 'Yes. The dupe took the dinars!'

"The judge was extremely surprised at this, and wanted to get to the bottom of it. So he started looking about, and decided that some one should walk around the tree and glance into the hollow. He looked inside and didn't see anything, since the man had already pulled himself up above the spot where the peephole was. The judge called for some wood, and it was gathered. Then he asked for a light, and started to smoke out the hollow.

"The rogue's father endured it for an hour; then his strength failed, and he shouted and called for help. The judge ordered him pulled out when he was at the point of death; while the rogue was punished and then fined. Then he went off home with his dead father on his back, and the dupe went away with his dinars.

"Now I have made this story up to teach you that the artful dodger is sometimes the one who gets fooled. And you, Dimnah, besides acting like a rogue, are trying to dodge the issues like an old woman. What you have reaped has been nothing except your deserts, and this will be the result of any business like yours. You are two-faced and double-tongued, and just as a river's fresh water only lasts up till the sea, and the integrity of a household only so long as a trouble-maker doesn't get into it, even so friendship lasts as long as two tongues don't split it up. The two-tongued person resembles nothing more than a snake, for the snake has two tongues, and your tongue secretes the same kind of poison.

"I have always been fearing lest the poison on your tongue

would disgrace me somehow. I hated your being around when I remembered wise men's warnings about shunning wicked people's company, even if they are kinfolk or friends or other connections. For a wicked man among your friends is like a snake whose master raises and fondles it, and then only gets stung.

"For it has been said: Hang around an intelligent, generous person, and get to know him; and though you may leave him, it is no hardship if you keep him company while his character is not praiseworthy. However, watch out for whatever bad habits he has, while taking advantage of his intelligence. Moreover, don't give up connection with the generous 'but unintelligent'[n] individual, but take advantage of his generosity, giving him the benefit of your intelligence. But flee as far as you can from the stupid villain.[20]

"Now I ought to flee from you and shun you, for how can you hope for loyalty and generosity elsewhere, when you have done that to your king, who honored and ennobled you? In this you are similar to the merchant who related that if there were a land where rats ate one one hundred minas of iron, it was beyond noticing if its hawks carried off elephants."

Dimnah said: "And how was that?"

Kalilah said: "

[N. The Mice Who Ate the Iron]

"Once upon a time in such and such a country, there lived a poor merchant who wanted to leave for elsewhere in order to gain a livelihood. Now he had a hundred minas of iron, and he left them in the care of a man he knew. Then he set out on his journey.

"When he returned after some time, he sought his iron which had been entrusted to his acquaintance, and found he had sold it and spent the proceeds. For he said: 'I placed your iron in a corner of my house, and the mice ate it.'

"The merchant remarked: 'Indeed I have been told that there isn't anything keener on iron than their teeth, nor easier than this kind of damage. Praise God that you yourself are safe!'

"The man was glad when he heard the merchant's statement, and he said to him: 'Come over and have a drink at my place today.'

"So the merchant promised to come back, and then went off. On the way, he met the former's small son, picked him up, and carried him off to his house and hid him. Then he went to call on the man, and there he was looking for the boy, and weeping and shouting.

"He asked the merchant: 'Have you seen my son?'

"The latter said to him: 'I saw him when a hawk was nearby, and it snatched a boy up. Perhaps that was he.'

"The man exclaimed: 'O wonders! Whoever saw or heard of a hawk carrying off a boy?'

"The merchant said: 'In a country where mice eat a hundred minas of iron, is it past believing that the hawks should carry off a boy, or even an elephant?'

"The man said: 'I ate the iron, and poison ate I. Give me back my son, and take your iron!'

"Now I have made this story up to teach you that when you betrayed your king whom you have found to be gracious towards you, there is no doubt but that you would betray some one else. Not one sensible person covets your friendship. I know there is not one scrap of decency in you, for nothing goes to pieces more quickly than affection squandered on some one disloyal, or a token of kindness towards an ingrate, or good breeding lavished on some one who pays no attention to it, or happiness granted one who has no judgment about it.

"I had no illusions about changing your character, for the bitter tree, even if it is painted with honey and butter, still bears only bitter fruit. I feared the effect your companionship would have on my mind and habits, for the company of good persons brings good results, and the company of evil ones occasions all sorts of evil. It is like the wind passing by a stench, and carrying off the odor with it; and when it passes by something good, it smells pleasant. I know how the weight of my words oppresses you, since numbskulls always make light of wise men, scoundrels vilify honorable people, and crooks spoil the straightforwardness of those they mingle with by their very crookedness."

Kalilah stopped talking at this point; and the lion finished with the bull. When he had killed him, his senses returned; and after his anger had subsided, he thought about what he had done. He could not do anything about it, and he said to himself:

"Perhaps the bull was sensible and good-natured after all. Perhaps he was innocent and slandered; so I have afflicted myself with misfortune in the long run, and can't make any amends for it."

Thus he was sad and regretful.

Dimnah noticed that in the lion, and he stopped talking to Kalilah. He ambled up to him, and said: "Whatever has saddened your majesty? God has fortified your hand and destroyed your enemy."

The lion said: "I am sorry for the bull's intelligence and noble character. I remember his companionship and how I am now deprived of it; so compassion for him has entered my heart."

Dimnah said: "Don't be merciful, your majesty, for the intelligent man is not merciful towards someone whose mischief he fears. The resolute king may detest a man and disapprove of him; so though he disapproves of him in person, he still deals with him, entrusting him with his administration when he knows he is settled and sensible, just as a man dislikes taking a disgusting and nasty medicine which he hopes will still do him some good. Perhaps he may love a man and be extremely fond of him, and still estranges and gets rid of him, fearing he may harm him, as a man cuts off his toe and throws it away when a snake has bitten it, fearing lest its poison will spread throughout his body and kill him."

The lion was consoled by his speech.

(Later however the lion investigated the bull's case and became uncertain about Dimnah's words and his accusation. Thus it became clear to the lion that Dimnah had been lying and done something wrong. He had broken his word to him; so he killed him in the worst possible way.)[21]

This is the story of two friends who loved one another and whom betrayal and deceit separated.

Thus Ends the Chapter of the Lion and the Bull

Chapter [II]

The Chapter of Dimnah's Trial

[Or the Artful Dodger]¹

(It being the chapter about one who wants to take advantage of someone else's predicament, but who gets a taste of his own medicine.)

ING 'DABSHALIM' said to 'Bidpai' the philosopher: "I have heard your story about the cunning and wily foe's tricks, and how he spoiled certainty through casting suspicion, thus changing affection into enmity. Now tell me, if you see fit, how the lion investigated Dimnah's crime till he executed him, and how 'Dimnah' tried to defend and justify himself."

Bidpai the philosopher said:

WE FOUND IN THE BOOKS which tell about Dimnah, that when the lion had killed Shatrabah, he regretted his haste and remembered his pledge. Among the lion's attendants and intimates was a leopard who was one of his noblest companions. He had very special rank, and lingered night and day in his privacy. After the lion had killed Shatrabah, he used to while away his nights by talking with his companions, so that their conversation might rid him of some of his grief and sorrow for having killed the bull.

Now one night the leopard was sitting up late, talking till it was time to go to bed. Then he left and went home. Kalilah and Dimnah's dwelling was near the lion's, and the leopard went up to their place to obtain a firebrand so he could get a light; and they were both sitting up with each other.

The leopard overheard their conversation, and kept quiet so he might hear what they were saying. He found that Kalilah had taken Dimnah to task and was upbraiding him. He was showing him how ugly his mind and conduct were, and pointing out the enormity of his crime. He scolded him for his treachery and kept telling him:

"You're the one who roused enmity between the lion and the bull after they had become companions, separated them after their friendship, and made them hate each other after they had come to terms. Your accursed intelligence and disloyalty have revealed your dealings and disclosed their true face and the consequence of your cupidity. Its result is unhealthy and its taste has turned out to be bitter.

"For even though its user is smooth-mannered and wants to sweeten its result, treachery has a bitter ending, and the chasm it produces is yawning and dangerous to whoever slips into it. I shall shun you and stop associating with and doing the same things as you; for really I am not sure you will not annoy me or covet something I have or betray me. For wise men have said: Shun suspicious people lest you yourself be suspected.

"So I am quitting your company and leaving you. I shall become a complete stranger to you, because of your evil disposition which brought about enmity between the king and his honest and trusty minister. You kept on in the same way, mixing matters up falsely until you put him beyond the pale and in such a difficult pass that he was killed wrongfully, innocent as he was."

Dimnah said: "What has happened cannot be avoided, so let matters stand as they are between you and me, and do something to rid the lion's mind of their effect. I loathe what occurred because of me, but envy and greed both brought me to it."

When the leopard heard their words, he went away secretly, hurrying to call upon the lion's mother.[2] He made her promise not to disclose the secret to the lion nor to anybody else. She promised him that, so he told her the story as it appeared from Kalilah's words and Dimnah's confession.

When morning came, the lion's mother set out to have an

audience with the lion. She found him broken-hearted and sad; so she said to him:

"Your sadness is no way to get back what has been taken from you, nor to force an advantage for yourself. You will not help by making it a tribulation, but rather weaken your constitution and wear yourself down physically. You will injure yourself, although you generally, thank God, have things turn out successfully and are observant enough to come to grips and deal with them.

"If you know that sorrowing can give you relief, then let us carry some of it for you; but if you know that you will not get anything out of it nor derive any advantage for yourself, then drop it and go look for something which can be of some use to you. Think over what has happened about Shatrabah until you can easily tell truth from falsehood."

The lion said: "How can I do that?"

The lion's mother said: "Wise men have said that whoever wants to distinguish one who loves him from one who hates him, and his enemy from his friend, should consider how people act just the same towards him as he acts towards them, for the most satisfactory evidence for a man is his own heart. Now these words of yours are an indication that your heart is bearing witness that you did what you did against your better judgment, while it was really quite obvious.

"So you must know, your chief mistake was in not restraining yourself and mastering your rage when you were told that about the bull; for then you would have gone over what you were told about him, considering it carefully, so that your heart would be satisfied that the evidence you were hearing was all a pack of lies. Hearts are exactly alike in that they agree secretly and openly. Compare the way the affair as well as his offence struck you at the time, and how it did the day after he was dead."

The lion said: "Since I killed him, I have really done much thinking, and been eager to find out what sort of charge could have been cooked up against the bull, and whether I had got angry at a single misdemeanor that could give a firm basis to my suspicion of him; and the more I think about him, the more I find only kindness and affection. I don't remember any evil on his part which I might say would have led him to envy me. I don't recall the slightest thing on my part where I see he would be induced to feel enmity towards me.

"So I would like to investigate his case and do my level best to track it down, although I know how that isn't any way to set right what I have already done. But I'd like the situation I was in to be known, and whatever I did either accidentally or on purpose. So tell me if you have heard something about the case which you can mention to me."

The lion's mother said: "Yes, a matter has reached me from one of your own people, and if it weren't for what wise men have said about telling secrets and revealing trusts—but leave off what doesn't benefit you, since there is no salvation from one whose harm we fear."

The lion said: "Indeed wise men have many ways of saying things and find different meanings for them and reveal them in various ways. There isn't anything in all this compelling us to keep [secrets], for everything has its proper place and time to be told. When its place is ready, the deed is cleared up thereby and advantage results; but if it is anywhere else, there is harm and things are ruined.

"Among those things which cause violent damage and which should not be mentioned, is wanting to tell something whose concealment is not suitable, nor disclosing something which should be kept secret. In this affair I don't see any excuse for secrecy nor any convenience in keeping quiet about it, for I see that whoever let you know about it, got a load off his own mind, while making you carry whatever good or evil there is in it. Thus you are right in disclosing it; you are only being cautious for your own sake. Forget whatever you promised about telling me!"

The lion's mother said: "I understand what you have said, and it is just as you say. If you were to keep on talking, I'd tell it, for I know how serious this affair is to you. When you are talking like this, I don't see how you let yourself be hindered from making an example of criminals and traitors and giving staunch support to good, trustworthy, and honest company; so tell me if your heart has not been turned against me."

The lion said: "My heart has not been turned; I hold no grudge against you; I am not suspicious of your sincerity; nor do I see any danger in your revealing this matter to me."

The lion's mother said: "Rather any harm lies in three points. One of these is ending my friendship with the person who knows this secret. Another is betraying the confidence I promised to keep. And the third is fear lest those who have been on familiar terms with me up till now will cut me off from their secrets."

The lion said: "The matter lies just as you have said: I don't want to get to the bottom of whatever you disapprove of, nor to rack my brains by becoming suspicious of your advice. So tell me the whole business, since you don't care to tell the name of the person who knows the secret nor reveal whatever he divulged to you."

So she informed him all about the story, without naming who had mentioned it. Some of what she said was this:

"Rulers and heads of state should not permit vicious treachery on the part of deceitful and slanderous individuals to continue, nor the cunning and corruption in mankind to corrupt people rather than to keep them honest. Now the first thing is to banish whoever corrupts mankind, and favor someone who will keep them honest and show leadership in administration. You are right in killing Dimnah, for it has been said: The ruination of highly important matters is due to two defects: divulging secrets, and trusting treacherous people.

"Now the one who sowed enmity between you and Shatrabah, that most loyal of ministers and the best of helpers, so that you killed him, is the traitor Dimnah, without counting his ignorance, shiftiness, and untrustworthiness. You have already learned about his underhandedness, and what he has been hiding from you is obvious, for you heard about it long ago. Your peace of mind and your court's lies in revealing these open secrets about him and disclosing his hidden thoughts. Kill him in punishment for his crime, and make good whatever your court has been suffering from his ill-doing. There is nothing like it to stimulate trustworthiness!

"Perhaps, o king, if you are lax by letting criminal people be pardoned and in thinking it over too much, you should know that none of those who have committed crimes have done Dimnah's. There is no greater fault than what Dimnah committed openly and secretly through his ignorance, shiftiness, and untrustworthiness. He incited the king against the most innocent of his ministers, one who was peaceful at heart and sincere to the core, so that he began to hate him and killed him on mere suspicion.

Then she added: "Indeed, I am not ignorant of what wise men have said about the exceeding merit of pardoning criminals, but it has merit only when it has nothing to do with individuals nor is a crime against people at large, which would only result in shame, and which rattlepates would utilize whenever they set about evil works. Thus the king would heighten the circumstances whereby people's respect for him would falter."

The lion then ordered his mother to leave.

At daybreak he sent for his courtiers and had the leading ones enter his presence. He fetched his mother, and she appeared in the council. Then he called for Dimnah, and he was brought.

When he was standing before him, the lion waved his hand as if to proceed to punish him.[3] When Dimnah saw that, he was sure of dying. He turned to someone who was close to him, and said in an undertone:

"Has anything happened which might sadden the king? Or why is he summoning you as I see?"

The lion's mother said: "The most serious matter is what has happened with you, and the most violent crime is yours, as well as how stupid you consider the king and how you killed the most innocent of his ministers."

Dimnah said: "I don't see how leaders can stop followers from speaking about a matter with serious implications. Already something of what they say has occurred: the more people strive to guard against evil, the more often they fall into it, for the king and his court have 'only[Sp]' such bad people.

"I know that it is said that whoever keeps company with evil individuals and does 'not[Sp]' know their 'deeds[Sp]', does not avert their evil effects by taking precautions against them. Thus ascetics cut themselves off from the world and choose solitude in the mountains rather than mingling with mankind. They prefer God's work to the work of His creation, since no one rewards goodness with good except God. As for those besides Him, their affairs result in all kinds of whims[4] since many of them are sinful.

"No one should aim at a straight-forward course more than a king, who is reliant upon God and flatters no one because he needs or fears him. It is even more proper for kings to request straightforward tokens of one another, and to reward well-tried people with their favor, since experience is finer than sound advice. It is well known, for I know it and so do all those present, that there was nothing between me and the bull to lead me to hold a grudge against him nor to wish him any misfortune. But I simply advised the king and let him know what I had found out about him as soon as I had the proof of what I mentioned. His attitude was very noble, and he was quite energetic in embarking upon his course of action.

"Yet I knew that some cheat or enemy might fear the same from me, so they have set out to cause my downfall and agreed upon killing me. I can only dread lest the reward for my good advice and fine token of loyalty would be to sadden the king till he ended by taking my life."

When the king heard Dimnah's words, he said: "Take him away and hand him over to the judge so they can investigate his case. I don't want to decide whether he is a good- or evil-doer unless the right and just side is apparent.

Dimnah prostrated himself before the lion, and then said: "Your majesty, there is nothing more apparent to the blind, or clearer in case of doubt, or firmer in guiding one out of dilemmas, than starting right in to see what can be accomplished in a matter. Indeed you know, o king, that fire is concealed in trees and stones, but one doesn't produce or use it except after working for it.

"If I were a crominal, I'd be frightened of my crime being revealed, exactly as this morning I find that I expect an enquiry and investigation to bring out the goodness of my affair, since I know I am innocent. Likewise daylight spreads an odor more, whether it is good or bad. If I knew there were any question about my having committed a sin or a crime, I'd be fleeing out into the world; but as I am attending the king's court,[5] I expect to be rewarded.

"But I'd like the king to order whoever is charged with investigating my case, to report every day on what he has uncovered about my treason or innocence, so that your majesty can form his own opinion and investigate some part of my case, and not act according to envious and hostile people's suspicions. What the king has already seen of their suspicions, such as in the case of the bull's hostility, makes it proper to refrain from killing me, for he knows my sincere counsel and how I protected his interests.

"Who doubts but that the king already knows my rank, my lowly state, and its slight esteem; I am unable to lift myself out of my condition of servitude nor to yearn for anything above me that is worth yearning for. Yet even if I am the king's slave, I still deserve justice from him, and I know that the king will grant me it as a favor in my lifetime and after my death.

"If the king has decided to hand me over to have my case examined and to enquire about my innocence, then I beg your majesty not to disregard my case and to have my pleas brought to him every day. But if the king, through some adverse stroke of fortune or because of my inability to thwart fate, is against doing anything and does not investigate my affair, overlooking the punishment these evil and cunning people are requesting without any previous fault on my part, then there is no one to whom I can turn except God, who discovers all our griefs.

"For indeed wise men have said: He who considered what is doubtful as certain when he should be suspicious of it, and thinks what he ought to consider certain is a lie; then the same happens to him as happened to the woman who gave in to her slave so that he dishonored and cast suspicion upon her."

The lion said to Dimnah: "How was that?"

Dimnah said:

[A. The Woman and Her Manservant]

"Once upon a time a merchant named Habal lived in the city of Tatharun in the land called Kashmir. He had a wife who was very favored by beauty. Next door to her lived a skilled painter, with whom the merchant's wife was friendly.

"The woman said to the man one time he came to see her: 'If you can think up some way I can recognize you when you come to me at night, without calling or throwing anything or rousing any suspicion, it will be easier for you and for me.'

"The painter said: 'Here's a trick which will please you: I have a sheet painted with many colors; one side is snowy white like the light of the moon, while the other is utterly black like the darkness of the murkiest night you might see. Its whiteness will catch your eye with its gleam in the darkness of the night; and its blackness will be apparent on a moonlit night.'

"So whenever he came to the woman, he used to put on the blanket, saying: 'When you see it, you will know it is I your friend; so come without being called.'

"One of the merchant's slaves entered while they were arranging this, and heard what they said. When some time had passed, the slave, who was the sweetheart of the painter's maid, asked her to lend him the sheet to show to a friend of his, saying that he would soon bring it back. So she gave him the sheet. He put it on, and met the woman at about the same time as the painter used to come to her.

"When she saw him, she didn't doubt but that it was her lover, so she went all the way with him and he had what he wanted of her. Then the slave returned the blanket to the maidservant, and she put it back in its place.

"All this while, the painter was away from home. When part of the night had slipped by, he returned home, put on the sheet, and went to the woman.

"When she saw the blanket, she came up to him and said: 'Whatever brings you back in such a hurry when you already had all you wanted in the first part of the night?'

"When the painter heard that, his spirits flagged, and he went off home. Then he called his maid and threatened to beat her; so she told him what sort of game it had been. The painter burned the sheet and was sorry for what he had done.

"I have only made this story up, your majesty, to teach you that appearances may be deceiving, and deception ruins its victim. Your majesty ought not to kill an innocent, upright, though sickly and imperfect person who has no protection in sight, nor any fault apparent except the tissue of scandal and the charge of treason.

"I am not saying this, your majesty, in awe of death; for even if it is awful, there is no escape from it for any living creature. If I had a hundred souls and knew the king wanted me to lose them, I should be very generous with them. If your majesty thinks that he will have peace and happiness by killing me, well, wise men have said: Whoever commits a sin or a crime and offers himself up to be killed instead of the righteous, will be rewarded by forgiveness and by escaping from evil in the other world.

"Now although I know that God has kept the king from being wicked and hard-hearted and slaying innocent souls on account of gossip-mongers and the accusation of profligates, I would like your majesty not to hurry the case without due investigation and scrutiny. Indeed, wise men have said: A man continually profits from good, seeing how much he has to do and how little he can criticize, so long as he recognizes it and keeps away from crimes during his lifetime."

While Dimnah was offering this plea, one of those sitting in the king's council stood up and said: "Your majesty, Dimnah is not saying this to strengthen the king's sense of justice or to praise his majesty, but only to dispel what has lodged in his mind concerning his evil actions."

Dimnah said: 'Woe on you! Is it any crime for a man to plead for himself? Is anyone closer to a man than himself? When he doesn't plead for himself, then who will attempt it? Who can advise me better than myself, or who can better receive advice? Wise men have indeed said: Whoever loathes and despises himself in preference to something else, is the most despicable robber, and is a bigger cheat and more to be shunned for his wickedness.

"What you are saying shows all those present how little wits you have and how ignorant you are in getting mixed up in talk. Whatever envy and hatred have taken possession of you have become manifest, and whoever listens to you knows you don't like anyone and are your own and others' worst enemy. It is unsafe for the like of you to be with anyone except criminals. So stop bothering the king with your presence or attending his court;[5] all you can do is make mistakes or show up your ignorance."

When the speaker heard Dimnah's words, he was silent. He did not answer back, and went out abashed.

So the lion's mother said: "You being what you are, it's a wonder how freely you can talk, answering anyone who speaks to you!"

Dimnah said: "Why are you watching every new piece of ill luck with one eye and hearing it with one ear? Everything has changed for the worse and been upset, and no one speaks the truth nor stands up for it, nor talks except according to his own whim Those in the king's court trust and rely upon him, and he showers affection upon them; they are not afraid to talk about their whims, adopting a right course when convenient, and abandoning it when it can't be helped, while he does not gainsay them."

The lion's mother said: "Look at this lying scoundrel who tackles just as big a thing as he wants, as if by snatching people's sight away, he were making himself out to be innocent."

Dimnah said: "A person like you 'has five⁹⁾' types: he who reveals secrets and does not keep them; the man who puts on women's clothes; the woman who puts on men's clothes; the guest who claims to be master of the house; and he who states in the king's council what is not asked of him."

The lion's mother said: "Don't you know how bad a thing you have done? Stop trying to talk yourself out of your guilt and show some respect!"

Dimnah said: "Whoever commits evil does not like anyone who is good, and will not help him avoid evil."

The lion's mother said: "O you deceitful liar! You are so bold to say such a thing that it is a wonder you are left alone!"

Dimnah said: "The deceitful liar is the one who is helped with your advice while he is strengthening his enemy. The latter does not thank the former nor recognize his one-time partner, but only wants to kill or injure him in some other way."

The lion's mother said: "Listening to your sermonizing and the stories you tell anyone who will talk to you, I am even more amazed at what has come about through your wheedling, cunning, and jealousy."

Dimnah said: "This would be the place for a sermon if it were heeded, and for stories if they did any good."

The lion's mother said: "O you lying traitor, considering the evil deed you committed, would you be bothered making up stories if you had any sense?"

Dimnah said: "The traitor only frightens one who is working under his protection and treats the person who reveals his foes as an enemy."

The lion's mother said: "So you expect, you liar, to save yourself with another speech that is just as criminal as the first?"

Dimnah said: "The liar pays back kindness with evil, good with wickedness, and tokens of friendship with fear. Now I have fulfilled all my promises and have kept my oath."

The lion's mother said: "What promise did you fulfill and what oath did you keep?"

Dimnah said: "My Lord knows that if I were lying, I would not dare talk falsely before Him nor twist out a lie."

When the lion's mother saw that Dimnah's speech did nothing except make the lion meeker, she began to falter. Fear possessed her, and an anxiety lest some of what Dimnah said would make him think he was innocent; so she said to the lion:

"Silence in the face of a quarrelsome person's argument is like acknowledging that what he is saying is right. In these circumstances, wise men have said: Silence gives consent."

Then she stood up, and she was raging. So she went out.

The lion gave orders concerning Dimnah, and irons were placed around his neck and he was locked up. He further ordered an enquiry about him.

Then the lion's mother said to him: "Personally, I have been hearing for some time now that Dimnah is sly. Besides, I am absolutely certain about what I have heard concerning his lying and making up excuses, and how often he has got out of messes dishonestly, without bothering to clear up his guilt. If you let him go on talking, he will keep you away from him by lying excuses; while if you kill him, you and your court will find a great deal of respite.

"So get a move on and kill him! Don't let forebearance get the better of you or let doubt stop you, for the mighty and the humble in your court know about Dimnah's bad reputation and his disgraceful conduct. At no hour of the night or day has there ever been the slightest doubt in my mind concerning his case. Whatever he serves you up in the way of excuses or absolving himself is because of his evil character, especially in the case of that innocent counsellor, Shatrabah, who was the best of your ministers. No day passes but I receive fresh proofs of Dimnah's evil disposition. They are certain and reliable, so you haven't any room left for doubt in his case.

"If you let him go on making speeches and weaving falsehoods, you will not be able to get around his wheedling and cunning, for his cheating and skill in spinning yarns will never fail. He will lie over and over again, since that is his rooted character and fixed disposition. Your peace of mind and that of your court rests in stopping the investigation and killing him for his crime."

The lion said: "It is a fact that in being familiar and intimate with kings, dignitaries quarrel among themselves. They are all jealous and envious of sensible and outstanding persons. I know that Dimnah's position has worried more than one of my attendants and family; but perhaps what I see and hear from his opponents is because of something like that.

"I dislike being hasty in his case, for one does not get rid of a dear and faithful friend except when it is justified and fate compels it. I don't find any excuse for following my own whim and acting hastily unless I investigate and make certain about it. So tell me the name of whoever told you this, a trustworthy and reliable person from what you assert."

The lion's mother said: "The trustworthy friend of mine who informed me is one you rely upon and entrust with your own secrets."°

The lion said: "Be happy and put your mind at ease, for now the idea of how to act has come to me!"

So the lion's mother went away with her mind at rest and in good spirits, and the lion sought his bed.

When Dimnah had been put in jail and shackles were placed on him, Kalilah was informed that Dimnah had been taken off to prison. Pity and sympathy possessed him, because they had been friends for so long and had been reared together, and for the brotherhood which had existed between them. So he went off in disguise to find him in jail.

Kalilah wept when he looked at him and saw how grief-stricken and sorrowful and distraught he was. Then he said to him:

"The mess you're in should be enough for you without my preaching; but it should not keep me from reminding you of your duty to all the advice and representations you have received. Every speech has its place. If I had failed to warn you in good times, when you needed me, I would be your accomplice in crime today.

"But your self-esteem got the better of you and overcame your intelligence and knowledge. I have already told you what they claim the wise men say: The intriguer dies before his time. They do not say: He dies before his time just because his life is cut off, but because so many things get mixed up that they ruin his life, like the plight you're in, where death would be more comfortable."

Dimnah said: "You always kept talking right along as hard as you could. You used to preach to me and advise me; but my evil mind and my eagerness to attain rank turned my head. I thought your advice was silly, like the sick person who is crazy about food which he knows will make his illness worse and harm his body; he spurns what he knows and follows his appetite. I knew I was sowing this trial for myself; but seed only sprouts in its time and season, even if you sow it ahead of time.

"This is the season for which I sowed, and my torment is increased by the fear that our relations look suspicious. I am therefore afraid that if you should be tortured, you will tell them what I have revealed to you. For after all, you are a person whose veracity is suspected by no stranger. But how would it be if his position were the same as mine?"

Kalilah said: "So I realize, and wise men have said that our bodies do not endure sudden torture, nor are they capable of refraining from talking about anything either true or false that will avert it. Now I don't see anything for you in this plight but to confess your fault and acknowledge your wickedness. Thus you can free your soul from the consequences of the next world through repenting what you have done. You have no means of escaping execution, so don't bring perdition down upon yourself in this fleeting life and the next."

Dimnah said: "You have spoken truthfully, and your advice is sound. I shall keep what you have said in mind. Still the affair is heart-rending, awful, critical. However, I shan't mention a word till I can tell what line they are going to follow in my case."

So Kalilah went off home grief-stricken, turning over everything concerning tribulation and evil in his mind. He kept this up till his stomach was upset, and he died before dawn.

Now they had a ʿwolf⁹⁾ locked up in the jail who was sleeping near Dimnah and Kalilah when they were together in the jail. He woke up just as they were talking, and heard everything they told each other. He took note of it, and kept quiet and did not mention anything.

The lion's mother got up next morning, and reminded the lion of Dimnah's case and treachery, saying: "Letting an evil-monger live is the equivalent of killing the pious; and whoever lets an evil-doer live is his companion in iniquity, or if a pious man, his companion in piety."

So the lion ordered the judge to expedite their investigation of Dimnah's case and the public enquiry, and that they uncover whatever implicated Dimnah in any crime, and Dimnah's excuse or pleas.

The judge went out to investigate the case, and some one was sent to fetch Dimnah. When they brought him, he walked into the middle of their council and took the floor.

So the leopard (who was one of the judges[Kn]) raised his voice and said: "You should know, all you courtiers, what sort of disillusionment has overtaken the king with the killing of Shatrabah. He is worried lest he acted wrongly and were deceived by Dimnah through lying imputation. Whoever wants to shed any light on the matter, let him rise up before us to investigate it, since you are obliged not to conceal any secret nor to hide any crime, as a sign of good faith.

"So let every man among you speak up with what he knows, since he should not withhold his hand from punishing anyone for his own whim or anybody else's. That is nothing more than releasing the culprit from the consequences of his guilt."

The judge said: "You have heard what has been told you, and none of you should conceal anything he knows on three grounds:

"One of them is truth, since unless you place small stock in the seriousness of justice, you are called upon to give evidence in the matter. Yet is there anything more serious than concealing the effrontery of someone who gets respectable people mixed up through slander, lying, and falsehood? Anyone who conceals things like that is (not[r]) innocent of committing the crime nor far from being accessory to the deed.

"The second is that when we punish the guilty, it acts as a deterrent to suspicious characters, and is an advantage to the king and his subjects.

"And the third is that when bad characters are driven from a land, its subjects enjoy better relations, honest people are happier, and happy folk are mutually helpful. Let every man of you say what he knows in order that judgment in this matter will be according to justice, and not following whim or fancy."

When the speaker had finished, those present kept silence. Not one of them uttered a word, for they knew nothing certain they could say on the score, and they did not care to talk about their conjectures for fear that what they said would be entered as evidence and lead to a conviction.

When Dimnah saw they were keeping quiet, he spoke up and said: "If I were guilty, I should be glad of your keeping silent about my case; but what power compels you when you don't know about any crime of mine?

"Now, whenever anyone is not known to have committed a crime, there is no way of proceeding against him, and he is declared innocent and acquitted. There is absolutely nothing you can say against me of your own knowledge, and you might as well know that if you speak up in my case, everything said will have its consequence sooner or later, and in my case that means life or death for me. Whoever suggests I should be put out of the way without evidence, or says anything suspicious or imaginary about my case, will have as a consequence what smote the physician who claimed to know what he didn't."

The judge said: "And what was that?"

Dimnah said: "

[B. The Quack Doctor]

"Once upon a time there lived in one of the cities of Sind, a physician who was successful and learned. Besides that, he had a fine reputation for his powers of restoring health to whatever people he applied his treatment or remedies.

"Now that physician died, and people utilized what was in his books. A foolish man claimed to know the science of medicine, and he became known among the people for it. The king of that city had a daughter who had married one of his brother's sons. She became pregnant and began to suffer the way pregnant women do, and found it rather painful.

"So the king set out to look for doctors, and he was told there was a physician living a few leagues away who was renowned for his knowledge of medicine. Thus he sent for him.

"When the messenger came to him, he found that his sight had failed due to his advanced age. So they described the girl's illness to him, and her symptoms. He prescribed a remedy called Ramharan for her.

"They told him: 'Mix this medicine for us.'

"He said: 'I am unable to see; so get all the ingredients together as I prescribe."

"So that ignoramus who claimed to know medicine came and informed them that he was acquainted with the remedy and knew how to compound and prepare it. The king ordered the dead physicians's books brought out for him, and let him into the storehouse to take whatever ingredients for the remedy were there.

"When he went in and they laid the ingredients out before him, he proceeded according to his own fancy and manner of acting. He took things without any knowledge or understanding, but just as matters struck him. He even chanced upon a deadly poison, and took and mixed it with his compound. Then he made the girl drink it, and she died an hour later.

"So the king made him drink some of the medicine he had mixed, and he died as well."

Dimnah added: "I have only told you this story to let you know how guilty one is who speaks⁷ in ignorance or takes action while in doubt."

So the king's steward⁸ spoke up at the request of the lion's mother, and said: "It is quite apt that the one who is not asking people for anything nor wanting anyone to doubt his case is this wretch marked with evil and the signs of debauchery. Indeed, wise men know what sort of judgment is passed on that!"

The chief judge said: "What are these marks and signs? For someone ignorant, it seems like placing overmuch stock in it."

The steward raised his voice and said: "Sages have said that whoever's left eye is small and squints a lot, whose nose leans over to the right, whose both eyebrows are set far apart, whose body hair sprouts three at a time, whoever watches the ground a great deal when he walks, and looks around every now and then; that individual combines treachery with a tendency to crime and envying honest men. These signs are all to be found on Dimnah!"

When he had ffnished his speech, Dimnah was greatly astonished at his words, and said: "Some things are judged by others, while God's judgment is straightforward and blameless. There is no injustice or enmity in it. If these and similar signs were what led to accuracy and truth, people would not be bothered arguing nor would anyone feel flattered at having done something fine. Neither could anyone be banished for committing evil, since the signs which make him act as he does cannot be altered. Because there is a reward for men of good works but no reward for men of evil ways, it is not because of these signs.

"If I had committed this disreputable deed, I would seek refuge in God. If I had done that, I should be wretched in another way, since the signs would have compelled me and I could neither have averted nor have kept them away. Besides, what you mention proves your small knowledge of the procedure of justice and its decisions: if it were as you say, I would not need any sign; they are created at the very same time as the person who has them, and they are born with him. The Maker does not place them on this day, or in this case, or for this thing, or as a judgment against their possessor and family, or when his innocence must be made known.

"Something nobody doubts in this is your error and ignorance; you have only heard something whose subtleness you do not grasp and you talk about it aimlessly. You are not a more skilful lawyer than those present, nor ahead of them in investigating cases; but you have spoken and been caught short. Your king is just like the physician: if you assert that good and evil rest only in signs, that is just as if there were no praise for the well-doer nor blame for the bad actor.

"I don't find anything but a plea for myself in this, nor are you doing anything but pleading for me and repeating what I would think of saying. You don't understand or consider what you are saying! In this you are like the man who said to his wife: 'Look to your own defects, you silly woman; then at others' faults.' "

Dimnah was asked: "How was that?"

Dimnah replied:

[C. The Peasant and His Quarrelsome Wives]

"Once upon a time the city called Burkhasht was entered by

an enemy. They killed all the people there, taking the women prisoners and dividing the captives amongst themselves.

"One of the enemy who was a ploughman drew two women. That man made them strip off their clothes and go without eating or drinking.

"Now a certain day, the ploughman went off with another man, leaving his two wives naked as they were to gather firewood on the mountain. One of the women found a clout, so she hid her shame.

"The other said to her master: 'Don't you see how this one is [not] going naked?'

"Her husband said: 'Shame on you! Why don't you look at yourself and cover yourself the same way as she has covered her private parts? Then start to talk.'⁹

"As for you, it is more surprising since I know how filthy your body is and how dirty you are. You are bold indeed to approach the king's food and bring it right up to his person, like some one free from blemish and clean of any stigma. I am not the only one among the intelligent people assembled here who is acquainted with your faults, and the only thing that kept me from showing them up before this was our affection for each other, for I disliked being the only one to reveal it.

"Since you are slandering and beginning to harm me through the enmity you have acquired, and are libeling me in the presence of the court without realizing how false it is, I am broadcasting what I know of your faults, starting with your filth, which I concealed. Anyone with it cannot claim to serve the king nor those under him!"

The steward said: "By any chance are you charging me with vice, you wretch?"

Dimnah said: "I am not charging you with any vice except what you actually have: the leprosy around your groin, the filth of your feet, and the disease of your testicles."

When the steward heard Dimnah say this, he stopped talking and all who were present stopped talking as a group, so that the judge ordered him taken off to prison.

'Now the lion's adviser who transmitted what Dimnah said and what they said about him was called*Sp* Rawzabah.ʸ When he heard this, he wrote it all down and brought it to the lion. When the lion saw that, he ordered the steward removed from office and not to appear before him nor to enter his house. The judge and another counsellor also wrote down what Dimnah had said. He ordered Dimnah returned to jail, and they took him away that same day.

There was an animal there called Jauzava[10] who was Kalilah's friend; he went to Dimnah and informed him about Kalilah's death.

Dimnah cried a great deal and said: "Why do I want to live now that my brother and true friend is dead? Whoever said the following spoke the truth: When a man comes to grief, evil befalls him from all sides and cares advance upon him, as has happened to me in losing Kalilah. He was my wealth and my mate, and he knew my good and evil secrets! If God has done this, praise be to Him who left me you in his stead, and who loves me well and will cherish and pity me as Kalilah did. Would you be so kind as to go to Kalilah's house and bring me whatever of his and mine you may find there?"

So he did this. Dimnah gave him Kalilah's share, and said to him: "You deserve it more than anybody else."

And he asked and begged him for love's sake to go before the lion and say something good about him and to let him know whatever the lion's mother should say about him.

He promised him it, and took what he gave him. In the morning Jauzava went to the lion and found the leopard and[11] the judge and some of his more respected friends entering his presence with a writ of what Dimnah had said in his attempt to justify himslef. The lion took the document and ordered them to leave him alone.

Then he sent for his mother, and read her that writ. She grew very troubled, and said: "If I speak harshly to you, o king, do not get angry!"

The lion said: "I am not getting angry; so say what you please."

She said: "I see you cannot distinguish what hurts you from what does you good. I reckon that Dimnah will be stirring up whomever you cannot rely upon nor trust, while you are spending your time investigating his case."

Then she got up and went out, and she was furious.

When it was morning, the judge sent for Dimnah. He was

brought, and the learned men consulted concerning him, but did not say anything about it.

So the judge said to him: "Indeed, if all those before you keep quiet and do not say a thing, it is because their opinions all concur in that you are guilty and there is no use in your living, since suspicion of you has settled in their hearts. I don't see anything better than for you to acknowledge your guilt in order to gain release from the next world's punishment and to get people talking well about you again, for two purposes.

"One of them is your ability to slip out of situations and to invent excuses which may keep you clear of trouble; and the other is because confessing your guilt will give you more peace of mind in the next world than you have in this. For wise men have said: Dying gracefully is better than living an ugly life."

Dimnah answered saying: "Judges should not judge according to their opinions or what people at large or in particular think. You know that thinking is not one whit sufficient in the case of truth, even if all of you consider me the perpretrator of this crime. I know better about myself than you do, and my own knowledge is surer since it is quite free from doubt. My case only seems ugly to you since you are like that, for you think I have poked my nose into someone else's business.

"What excuse can I offer you for poking my nose into my own business, to lie about my own soul and deliver it up to be killed in full knowledge of its innocence? So far as I am concerned, it is a very important soul and the one I ought to honor first. If I did that with the closest or furthest of you, it would be against my religion and character.

"Stop talking like this about me! If you have any good sense, you have still taken the wrong stand; while if you are trying to cheat me, the ugliest form of swindle is what is premeditated: cheating and cunning are not the qualities of an upright judge. Don't you know that your verdict is a piece of law and can become a precedent? Every case a judge handles is part of law and a precedent which straight-living people take as part of their straight living; while any error of his becomes a part of justice for people looking for loopholes.

"My greatest misfortune is also that you will always remain a person of excellent sense and judgment in men's minds; you may turn things your own way in my case, ignoring your acquaintance with verdicts and decisions and relying upon conjectures, which vary according to the circumstances of each case. 'Watch out that what happened to the man who said what he didn't know or see, doesn't happen to you!"

The head of the army and the judge said: "How was that?" Dimnah said:

[D. The Satrap and the Parrots][11]

"Once upon a time in a certain town there lived a man called^Sp a satrap^Y who was noble and handsome, and had a beautiful, good, and faithful wife. This nobleman had a falconer who liked his wife and often made love to her, while she did not turn her head towards him; and he threatened her in an ugly fashion. When she spurned him, he thought of getting her in wrong with her husband.

"One day he went out hunting, and caught two young parrots. He separated them and taught one to say: 'I saw the porter in bed with my lady!'; and taught the other to say: 'I will not tell tales!'

"He taught the young birds in Bactrian, which was not known in that country. He took them and presented them to his master, and they talked to him. He liked them, for he did not know what they were saying.

"One day some guests arrived from Bactria. When they had eaten, he ordered the birds brought out to amuse them, and they began to talk. When they heard what the birds said, they looked at each other and lowered their heads in shame at what they heard.

"One of them said: 'Do you know what they are saying? Don't get angry at us if we tell you. For they are talking in the Bactrian language.'

"He said: 'I shan't get angry, for I'd like to know.'

" 'Do you know one is saying: "The porter goes to bed with my lady!"; and the other says: "I will not tell tales!" Now we have a law that we cannot stay in the house of a wicked hostess.'

"When they told that, a servant who was standing nearby said: 'That's true, and I am a witness for it, since I often heard it and didn't dare say so.'

"When the master of the house realized that, he ordered his wife executed.

"She begged him to make sure of what they said, saying: 'Ask and beg the parrots if they know any more of the Bactrian language, and they will find your falconer did it, for he asked me to make love to him and I didn't want to!'

"They did so and saw they did not speak any more; so everybody understood that the falconer had taught them. When they saw that the wife was blameless and the falconer was lying, he was summoned. He entered with a bold front[Sp] and a greyish hawk in his hand.[r]

"The woman said to him: 'Say if you saw me do what you say!'

"He said: 'Yes.'

"When he had said this, the hawk leaped into his face and clawed out his eyes.

"The woman said: 'You see God's justice, you traitor, which still came and seized you, since you gave false witness against me concerning what you didn't know and what hadn't occurred.' "

Dimnah said: "I gave you this story so that you can keep from doing what the falconer did; for God judges whoever does that both in this world and in the next."[Sp]

So they wrote all that down, and took it off to the lion. He looked at it, called his mother, and handed it to her.

This is what she said to him: "I was beginning to get very worried lest Dimnah were twisting you around his finger with his shrewd and cunning ways, till he would kill or ruin you. My worst worry was how he managed to stir up trouble against you through cheating and slandering your minister and true friend, so that you killed him through no fault of his own."

Her speech made an impression upon the lion, and he said to her: "Tell me who it was told you what he had heard about Kalilah and Dimnah's conversation. If I kill him, that will be one argument for me when I face Dimnah."

She said: "I dislike disclosing a secret which has been told me, so as not to commit what wise men have forbidden by revealing a secret; but I'll see if the person who told me the matter will release me from not mentioning it to you, or if he will take it upon himself to tell you what he heard instead."

Then she went away and sent for the leopard. He came to her, and she reminded him of his fine rank with the lion, and how he ought to do him a service in the line of justice by giving evidence that no man like him should hide. Besides, it was only right for him to render assistance and help to someone who had been injured, strengthening his case for the day of resurrection. She kept on till he went and gave his evidence about what he had heard Dimnah and Kalilah saying.

When the leopard gave his evidence against Dimnah, the beast who had been jailed and had heard what Kalilah said to Dimnah that night he had come to see him in prison, stated: "I have some evidence; take me out to tell it!"

The lion sent for him, and he bore witness against Dimnah, quoting how Kalilah had scolded him for having come between the lion and the bull through lying and slander so that the lion had killed the latter. And how Dimnah had admitted it.

The lion asked him: "What kept you from giving us your evidence against Dimnah the time you heard it?"

The beast said: "Mine being the only evidence prevented me from doing so, since it couldn't influence a verdict nor refute any opponent. I didn't feel like talking to no avail."

Two pieces of evidence had both gone against Dimnah, so the lion sent them to Dimnah and confronted him with what had been said. The lion ordered bonds placed upon him; then he was placed in solitary confinement until he died of hunger and thirst.

This is what became of Dimnah's case. Such is the
punishment of covetousness and what happens
to envious and lying people.

Here Ends the Chapter of Dimnah's Trial

Chapter III

The Chapter of the Ringdove

[Or the True Friends][1]

ING 'DABSHALIM[n] said to 'Bidpai[n] the sage: "I have heard your speech about the two close friends whom a scheming traitor separated. Now tell me a story about how two sincere friends get to know and are able to be of benefit to each other."

The clever wise man said: "The intelligent individual thinks nothing is equal to an upright friend, for friends are helpful in all sorts of good, and generous in times of hardship. One of these stories is the story of the crow, the ringdove, the mouse, the tortoise, and the deer."

The king said: "How was that?"

The philosopher said:

[A. The Pigeons, the Fowler, and the Mouse]

ONCE UPON A TIME IN THE KINGDOM of 'Duzat near the city called Muzne[Sp)] there was a place full of game where hunters used to hunt. In that spot there was a mighty tree with many branches thick with leaves, and in it was the nest of a crow 'called Geba[Sp)].

One day when the crow was perched in the tree, he saw a hunter who was so ugly you could see he had an evil disposition. On his shoulder he was carrying a snare, and in his hand a stick, and he was approaching the tree.

The crow was terrified of him, and he said: "Some business must be bringing this man here. I shall see what he is going to do!"

The fowler approached, set up his snare, scattered his grain, and hid in a nearby spot. It was only a short time until a pigeon called a ringdove happened by. She was the mistress of many doves who went along with her. The ringdove noticed the grain, but not the net, and so they all fell into it. Then the hunter came hurrying up quite excited, and all the pigeons began to raise a great stir, struggling against each other in every direction.

The ringdove spoke to them: "Don't leave anyone helpless in your struggle, nor be more concerned about yourself than your friends! But let's all get together and perhaps we can carry off the net and save some ones' lives."

So they did that, lifting the net into the air. The hunter followed them, thinking they could not get very far before the net would feel heavy and they would drop down.

The crow said: "I am going to follow them till I see how things turn out for them and the fowler."

The ringdove looked around and saw the hunter was still following, not having given up hope of catching them. She said to her friends:

"I see that the fowler is intent upon catching us. If he sticks to his resolve, you won't be able to hide from him; but let's head towards ploughed[2] and settled country,[3] where we will soon hide our whereabouts. Then he will go away despairing of us.

"Now since we are in such a tight spot, I know of a place near settled and cultivated land where there is the hole of a mouse who is friendly with me. If we go to him, he will cut this net for us, and we will not be chided by him."

So they went off to where the ringdove had said. They were lost sight of by the fowler, and he went away in despair. The crow did not go away, but rather wanted to see what sort of trick they would use to get out of the snare, so he might learn and use it in case of need.

When the ringdove brought them to the mouse, she ordered the doves to settle down. They did so, and found a hundred openings around the mouse's hole which he prepared from times of fright, and had tested cannily. The ringdove called him by name, and his name was 'Zirak'[n].

The mouse answered her from within his hole, saying: "Who are you?"

She answered: "I am your good friend, the ringdove."

So he hurried out to greet her.

When he saw her in the snare, he said to her: "What has thrown you into this scrape, when you're so clever?"

The ringdove said: "Don't you know that there isn't anything good or bad but it is fated to strike someone in his due time and season? Fate has thrown me into this scrape since it showed me the grain and blinded my sight as to the snare, so that I fell into it along with my companions.

"My case and my lack of means of thwarting fate are not surprising, for people stronger and more dignified than I do not manage to thwart fate. The sun and the moon are eclipsed when that is decreed, fish are caught in the depths of the sea, and birds are brought down out of the air. The reason that the weakling earns what he needs is the same as when something comes between the resolute individual and the object of his desires."

Then the mouse began to gnaw the knots in which the ringdove was caught.

The ringdove said to him: "Start with my companions' knots, and then come to mine!"

She repeated this several times; but each time the mouse would not heed what she said. Then he said to her:

"You keep talking as if you don't pity yourself nor are really concerned about your own fate."

The ringdove said: "Don't blame me for what I am ordering you to do. The only thing that forces me to do so is that I have assumed the leadership of all these pigeons, and thus they have their rights over me. They have fulfilled their obligations about obeying and advising me, so that through their obedience and assistance, God has freed us from the owner of the net. I am afraid that if you begin by cutting my knots, you will get tired and be lazy in finishing off what remains of theirs; while I know that if you begin with them and leave me to the last, you will not want to stop your efforts even though langour and weakness overtake you."

The mouse said: "This is why people like you better and better, and long for you so much."

Then the mouse began to gnaw until he had finished, and the ringdove and her pigeons flew home in safety.

[B. The Crow, the Mouse, and the Tortoise]

When the crow saw how the mouse had finally freed the pigeons, he wanted to make friends with him, and said:

"Am I not likely to have the same thing happen to me as happened to the pigeons? Wouldn't I be assured against it through the mouse and his affection?"

So he approached the mouse's hole and called him by name. The mouse answered: "Who are you?"

He said: "I am [Geba] the crow, and my business is such and such. I saw what you accomplished and how loyal you are to your friends, and how God has thereby been able to benefit the doves. What I have seen makes me want to be friends with you, and that is why I am here."

The mouse said: "There is no reason for you and me to be on close terms. An intelligent man should only look for something which he can attain and stop hunting for what doesn't exist. Otherwise he will be considered ignorant. It is just like the man who wants to make ships run on land, and carts on water. How can there be any intimacy between you and me, since I am food and you're the one who'll eat me?"

The crow said: "Consider how if I consumed you as food, it wouldn't be of any use to me; while if you keep on living and I can win your affection, I shall be safe as long as I live. You are not right in sending me away disappointed, when I come and seek your affection, since your fine character has been evident to me even if you don't want to display it. Still, the intelligent person does not hide his virtue; but rather he reveals it to the best of his ability. It is like musk, which is not prevented from spreading its odour, although it is hidden and sealed. You won't 'change⁽ᵠ⁾' your own character nor withhold your affection and kindness from me!"

The mouse said: "The worst form of enmity is natural enmity, of which two kinds are to be found:⁴ 'mutual⁽ᵖ⁾' enmity like that between the elephant and the lion, for sometimes the lion kills the elephant, and sometimes the elephant kills the lion; and 'one-sided⁽ᵖ⁾' enmity whose harm derives from one person opposing another, like the enmity between me and the cat, and between you and me. Enmity on my side is not because of the harm I can inflict upon you, but the harm which I may receive from you.

"There is no relief from natural enmity, except through sin which brings one back again to enmity; nor is there peace from enmity through inheriting wealth or marrying into the opposite side, for even if you heat water and keep on heating it for a long time, it is still not prevented from extinguishing a fire when thrown on it. So whoever bears enmity and wants to become reconciled is just like the person who owns a snake and carries it in his 'bosom℘).5 An intelligent man does not make friends with a clever foe."

The crow said: "I understand what you have said, and you are really displaying your good nature. You know I am telling you the truth and not making things difficult between you and me by saying: 'There is no way for us to get better acquainted,' for intelligent and high-minded men long for some connection or way to every kind of goodness.

"Affection between honest men is hard to break and easy to join. That is like a gold jar which is hard to break and simple to restore and repair, even if it has been shattered. Affection between evil men is easy to break off and hard to establish, like the earthenware jar which is broken through the least defect and then never can be pieced together again.

"A high-minded man develops an affection for another high-minded man upon one meeting or through knowing him one day, while an evil man does not approach anyone except with dread or for some purpose. Now you are high-minded and I am in need of your friendship, so I am planting myself at your doorstep and not tasting food till you swear brotherhood with me!"

The mouse said: "I accept your brotherhood for I have never sent away any person in need, nor do I want to shirk a duty; although if you should betray me, don't say: 'I found the mouse short-sighted and easy to fool!' "

Then he came out of his hole and stood by the door.

The crow said to him: "What is holding you at the door of your hole and keeping you from coming out and being friends with me? Are you suspicious of me after all?"

The mouse said: "Worldly people offer one another two things, and get friendly because of both of them: to fill their hearts and to fill their hands. As for those who exchange love for their hearts' sake, they are sincere and unalloyed. Those who exchange love for their hands' sake, help each other and are fair-weather friends so long as each can get something he needs out of the other. The person who only does some service when he is looking for a reward or to gain a few worldly advantages, resembles in his giving and taking the fowler who tosses grain to the birds not through any desire to serve them, but desiring his own advantage. So yielding one's heart is finer than lending one's hand.

"I am relying upon your giving yourself, and I shall grant you the same for myself, though I can do nothing to get rid of any evil thought ⟨you$^{Y/CeD)}$ may hold. However, I know that you have some companions who are essentially the same as you, while their opinion of me is not the same as yours; thus I am afraid lest some of them may see me with you and slay me."

The crow said: "One of the signs of a true friend is that he is a friend of his friend's friend, and an enemy of his friend's enemy. I haven't any companion or friend who would be dear to you, and it would be very easy for me to separate from some one like that, just as a grower of sweet-smelling herbs, when some kind of plant which can harm and spoil them sprouts among his herbs, kills and pulls it up along with his sweetgrass."

Then the mouse came out to meet the crow, and they both shook hands and became firm friends, each of them treating the other as a friend. They spent several days at this, or whatever God disposed.

⟨Some days later$^{Y/CeD)}$, the crow said to the mouse: "Your hole is near the highway of men, and I am afraid lest ⟨some boys should throw a rock at you$^{y)}$. Now I know of a secluded spot, where I have a friend among the tortoises. It is abounding in fish, and I shall find something to eat from them. I'd like to go there and live off them in safety."

The mouse said: "Why shouldn't I go along with you, since I dislike this place of mine so much?"

The crow said: "What don't you like about your place?"

The mouse said: "I know some stories and tales I'll recite to you if we go to this place we have in mind."

So the crow took the mouse by the tail and flew with him till he reached where he wanted to go. When they neared the place where the tortoise was, and the tortoise saw a crow carrying a mouse, he got frightened and dived into the water, since he did not recognize his friend.

The crow put the mouse on the ground, perched on a tree, and called the tortoise, (who was called Afza$^{sp)}$, by name. She knew his voice, and came out to welcome him, asking him where he had come from. The crow told her his story from the time he had followed the pigeons, and how matters had gone subsequently, including the mouse's case until they both reached her.

When the tortoise heard the mouse's story, she was astonished at his intelligence and loyalty, and welcomed him, saying: "Whatever brought you to this land?"

And the crow said to the mouse? "Where are those stories and tales which you stated you would tell me? Tell them now when the tortoise is asking you about them, for she should be on the same footing as I am with you."

[B.1 The Mouse and the Monk]

The mouse began to tell his story, saying: "My first home was in the city of (Marut$^{n)}$,[6] in the house of a man who was an ascetic. The ascetic had no family, and they brought him a basket of food every day. He would eat what he needed, and then place the rest of the food back in the basket, and hang it up in the house.

"I would lie in wait for the monk to go out, and when he did, I would jump into the basket and not leave any food there without eating it or throwing it to the other mice. The monk strove many times to hang this basket up so I could not reach it, but he couldn't do it.

"Then the monk lodged a guest with him one night, and they ate supper together. Finally they reached the point in their conversation where the monk said to his guest: 'From what country do you come, and whither are you bound?'

"The guest had been all over the world, and seen its wonders; so he began to tell the monk about the countries he had passed through and what sort of things he had seen. During the pauses, the monk kept clapping his hands to scare away the mice.

"The guest got angry at this, and said: 'I am telling you a

story, and you keep smacking your palms as if you were making fun of what I'm telling you. Whatever made you ask me in the first place?'

"The monk apologized to the guest, saying: 'I certainly want to hear your story, but I have been clapping to scare off the mice which are bothering me. I can't leave any food in the house without their eating it up.'

"The guest said: 'Is it one mouse or many?'

"The monk said: 'Besides several mice, there is one which pesters me, and I can't find any means of getting rid of it.'

"The guest said: 'This can only be for some good reason. You remind me of the words the man said to his wife: "There is some reason this woman sold her husked sesame for un-husked." '

"The monk said: 'How was that?'

"The Guest said;

[B.1a The Husked and Unhusked Sesame]

'Once I lodged with a man in such and such a city, and we ate supper together. Then he made up a bed for me, and the man went off to his own bed and his woman companion. Between them and me there was a reed partition; so I heard the man and his woman talking at night.

'I listened hard to their conversation, and the man was saying: "I want to invite a certain individual to eat with us tomorrow."

'His wife said: "How do you invite people to share your food when you haven't sufficient for your own family? You are not a man to have anything left over nor to store it up."

'The man said: "Do you begrudge me anything we hand out and help to feed someone with? Keeping everything and storing it up will perhaps have the same effect as with the wolf."

'The woman said: "What happened to the wolf?"

'The man said:

[B.1b The Greedy Wolf]

' "A certain huntsman went out one morning with his bow and arrows, eager for the hunt and the chase. He had not gone very far before he shot a deer and brought it down; so he picked it up and turned back to his family.

' "Now it happened that a boar appeared in his road, and when the boar saw the man, he charged him. The man dropped the deer, and taking his bow, he fired a shot at the boar which pierced him in the middle. Still the boar managed to reach the man and deal him a blow with his tusk. The bow and arrows flew out of his hand, and they both dropped down dead together.

' "Then a hungry wolf came along, and when he saw the man, the deer, and the boar, he started to count on lots to eat. He said:

' " 'I ought to store up what I can, since one is not foresighted unless he anticipates by saving things up and putting them aside. I shall hasten to bury what I have found in a safe place, and content myself with this bow-string for today.'

' "Then he approached the bow to eat its string, and when he had cut the thong, the bow snapped. I shot back and hit him in the vital part of his throat, and he died.

' "I have only told you this story so you can know that being too greedy may have unhealthy consequences.

'The woman said: "Fine, since you say so. We have some rice and sesame which will be enough food for a party of six or seven. I shall get up to prepare the food tomorrow morning, and shall have whatever you want ready for dinner.

'So the woman arose early in the morning and took the sesame and peeled it. Then she spread it out in the sun to dry, and said to her husband's boy$^{Y/CeD)}$: "Keep the birds and dogs off this sesame."

'The woman went away on some errands and chores of hers. The boy got careless, and a dog went up to that sesame and 'spoiled$^{Y/CeD)}$ it.[7] The woman noticed it, and as she found it was dirty, she did not want her guests to eat it.

'So she went off to the market and exchanged it for some unhusked sesame of exactly the same amount. She did so while I was in the market, and saw what she was doing, and I heard a man saying:

' "Why has she given this husked sesame for unhusked sesame?"

" 'Like what I have described is this mouse which you say jumps into the basket whenever you hang it up, for it must have some reason for being able to do that ahead of his companions. Fetch me a spade ʿand dig up his hole and find out what it can be.ⁿ.'

"Then the guest went with it while I was in another hole than my own, listeneing to their conversation. Now there was a place in my hole where there were a thousand dinars. I don't know who put them there, but I used to spread them out and amuse myself with them, and I felt important every time I remembered them.

"So the guest dug up my hole until he reached the dinars, and then he took them and said to the monk: 'This is what gave that mouse strength enough to jump where he did, because wealth increases one's strength and insight. You will see that from today on, the mouse will not be able to show the strength and daring that he could in the past.'

"I heard what the guest said, and realized that I was broken down and lacking in what I had been so proud of, and I moved from my hole to another one. In the morning I knew that my standing among the mice had gone down, and that they had little regard for me: they insisted that I should do what I had been in the habit of doing by jumping into the basket. I was too weak to do it, so they shunned me and began to talk among themselves: 'Fate has finally caught up on this fellow and he will soon be in want, so that some of you will be looking after him.'

"So they all snubbed me and went over to my rivals, pouncing upon my defects and shortcomings with anyone who would talk about me. Then I said to myself:

" 'I see that one's brethren and family, friends and helpers, follow nothing but wealth; nor do I see any manliness apparent except with riches, nor any insight and strength. Whenever a man without wealth wants to reach some objective, I find that poverty keeps him away from his desire, cutting him off from attaining his aim just as water from the summer rains is cut off in the coulees[8] and never reaches the sea nor even a river before the earth absorbs it, since it has ʿnoˢᵖ⁾ constant flow with which to reach its goal.'

"I found that whoever [has money] has friends, and whoever has no money has neither family, children, nor fame, nor is anyone without money considered intelligent by people in this world nor in the next. When a man falls in need, his friends cut him off and he becomes contemptible to those who are close to him. He may even be forced to earn his livelihood and seek it for himself and his family, going out into the world and ruining his future life so that he loses both this world and the next.[9]

"'There is nothing stronger than poverty; a tree growing in a$^{Y/CeD}$ saltmarsh', gnawed all over, is better off than a poor man who needs what others have$^{Y/CeD)}$. Poverty is the beginning of every misfortune and calls people's hatred down upon its victim so that he is thereby deprived of intelligence and virtue, his knowledge and breeding slip away from him, and he becomes a butt for suspicion and shorn of modesty. Whoever is shorn of modesty finds his happiness flees him and he is hated; whoever is hated is doomed; whoever is doomed is depressed; whoever is depressed loses his mind and forgets what he has remembered and understood; and whoever is affected in his mind, memory, and understanding, talks and acts more against himself than for himself.

"I find that when a man becomes poor, he is suspected by whoever has trusted him, and whoever thought well of him thinks ill of him. If someone else commits a crime, then they blame him, and he becomes the object of every sort of suspicion and evil thought. There is no motive for praise in a rich man which does not become a fault in a poor man: for if he is daring, he is called foolhardy; if he is generous, he is called a wastrel; if he is meek, he is called weak; if he is serious, he is called dull; if he is talkative, he is called a chatterbox; while if he is silent, he is called stupid.

"Death is easier than destitution which compels the destitute to beg, and especially to beg from rotten tightwads. If a high-minded man were forced to put his hand into a sea-monster's mouth, take out its poison, and then swallow it, that would be easier for him than begging from a dirty miser.

"It has been said that one who is afflicted with some bodily ailment which he cannot get rid of, or is separated from his loved ones and friends, or is in exile where he doesn't know any lodging or resting place and from where he does not expect to return, or is in such destitution that he is obliged to go begging; then life is a death for him, and death brings him peace.

"Perhaps indeed the man dislikes begging when he is in need, and is thus brought to theft and robbery. Theft and robbery are worse than what they supplant, for it has been said that silence is better than falsehood, acting stupid than violence and injury, and misery than the ease and comfort which man's wealth affords.

"Then I saw that when the guest had pulled out my dinars, he had divided them with the monk. The monk put his share in a purse which he placed by his head at night. I hoped they would thus restore some of my strength and that some of my friends would come back to me. So I went while the monk was sleeping, and creeping close to his head, I found that the guest was awake. He had a stick, and he struck me a painful blow on the head with it; so I ran off to my hole.

"When the pain subsided, hankering and greed overpowered me, and they finally overcame my better judgment; I crept out as eagerly as I had in the first place till I was quite close, while the guest lay in wait for me. He hit me again on the head with the stick, so that it drew blood. I crawled along, partly on by back and partly on my belly, till I entered my hole and fell down in a faint. Such a pain seized me as made me ʿhate ⁿ⁾ wealth so much that if I hear it mentioned today, it makes me start to ʿshudder and dread it ˢᵖ⁾.

"Then I reflected and found that the trials of this world are only forced upon people through greed and gluttony, and the worldly individual is constantly tormented by misfortune and weariness since he is obsessed by greed and gluttony. I saw that the difference between generosity and stinginess is great, and that moving along with circumstances and undertaking distant journeys in search of wealth is easier for a miser than for a generous person to stretch out his hand to snatch money.

"I don't see anything like contentment. I have heard wise men saying: There is no better sense than good management, no piety like ʿkeeping from doing harm ^Y/CeD⁾, no ʿbeauty ⁿ⁾ like a fine character, and no riches like contentment. The most fitting patience is where there is no way of changing one's lot. And it is said: The finest of deeds is mercy, the beginning of affection is familiarity, the origin of understanding is knowledge about what is so and what is not so, and peace of mind and beauty lie in turning away from the unattainable.

"Thus I reached the point where I was satisfied and compla-
cent, and so I moved from the monk's house to the country."

The mouse, who was the crow's friend, said to the tortoise: "I
had a friend among the pigeons whose friendship started long
before the crow's. Later the crow mentioned the affection between
you and him, and told me that he wanted to visit you, so I was
anxious to come along. I dislike being alone, for there isn't any
happiness in the world that can compare with the companionship
of friends, nor is there any grief which can compare with separation from friends. I have experienced it, and have learned that an
intelligent man should not seek more from the world than enough
to keep himself from want and annoyance.

"What will avert that is trifling: only food and lodging when he
is helped by good-heartedness and easy conditions in the country.
If some man were granted the world and all it contains, only the
pittance that keeps want from his door would do him any good;
any more than that has to be put in a place of its own, and does
not offer him 'anything but the chance to look at it like anybody
else$^{Y (cD)}$. I have approached the crow with that idea in mind, and I
shall be a brother to you just the same, and live only for you!"

When the mouse had finished speaking, the tortoise answered
him with sweet and kind words, saying: "I have heard what you
have said and 'how beautifully you have phrased it^{n}; but I see that
you are recalling matters which are still on your mind. You feel
strange amongst us, although it shouldn't be that way. You know
that fine words are only brought to fruition through deeds, for if a
sick man knows the remedy for his illness and doesn't use it, then
his knowledge does him no good, nor does he find any rest or
relief.

"Make use of your understanding and employ your intelligence:
stop feeling sad because you are not wealthy. A manly person is
honored even without having money, just as the lion is feared
even when he is crouching; while a rich man who has no manliness is considered soft even if he is very wealthy, like the dog
whom people despise even if he has a collar set 'with gold$^{Y \ and \ P)}$.

"Don't you worry about feeling strange, for an intelligent man
never feels strange nor goes abroad without taking along enough
intelligence to suffice him; like the lion who never turns anywhere
but he has enough strength to give him his living. Act so as to

make your soul worthy of as much good as possible, for if you do that, goodness will come looking for you like water that seeks a slope and waterfowl water. Excellence is only granted to the observant, shrewd, and searching [mind], while the lazy, hesitant, and procrastinating individual enjoys very little distinction, just as a young woman does not find any advantage in an old man's company.

"Don't let it sadden you to say: 'I had money and now I am in want'; for money and the rest of this world's goods come suddenly and go just as quickly, like the ball which both goes up fast and falls swiftly. It is said that there are some things which are never firm or constant: a cloud's shadow, an evil person's friendship, craving for women, false praise, and much wealth.

"An intelligent man never feels glad with much money nor sad with little, but his wealth lies in his intelligence and the good works he has already accomplished; for he trusts that he cannot be deprived of what he has done, nor be reproved for anything left undone. He ought not to overlook what concerns his after-life, laying up store for it, since death only comes unexpectedly, and there is no known time between it and anyone. You can do without my warning, since what will befall you is obvious; but I consider myself obliged to determine what is right for you, since you are our friend, and whatever we both have is yours for the taking."

When the crow heard how the tortoise answered the mouse so favorably, and what kind words he said to him, he was pleased and gladdened by it. He said:

"You have made me very happy and done me a favor. You ought to be very pleased with yourself, since I am so happy; for the foremost people in this world, who are happiest and enjoy the best reputation, are those who do not desert their friends and companions. They are easy to get along with, and are constantly thinking up ways to make them happy themselves. They are behind them in case of need or in business, for when a respectable man stumbles, he does not get up again except with another respectable man's assistance, just as when an elephant gets stuck in the mud, it does not get out except with the help of the elephant.

"An intelligent man 'is always⁽ᴾ⁾' known for his work; and no matter how much he has done, even to risking his life and exposing it to a known danger, he does not consider it a mistake but knows that he is risking the perishable for the enduring, and is buying the greater with the lesser. The most enviable people have many calls for help and requests for assistance, for no one is counted rich who does not share his wealth."

[C. The Deer]

While the crow was talking, a deer came running up to them. The crow, the mouse, and the tortoise were startled by him; so the tortoise jumped into the water, the mouse went into his hole, and the crow flew off and settled on a tree. The deer approached the water and drank a little of it. Then it stood up terrified, and looked around.

The crow then hovered in the sky to see who would be hunting the deer. He looked in every direction and did not see anything, so he called to the tortoise to come out of the water, and said to the mouse:

"Come out for there isn't anything here for you to be afraid of!"

So the crow, the mouse, and the tortoise gathered at their spot. The tortoise said to the deer, when she saw it watching the water and not drinking:

"Drink if you are thirsty; don't be afraid, for there are no grounds for your fear."

So the deer approached them. The tortoise greeted him and asked for his health, saying: "Where have you come from?"

He said: "I have been in this wilderness while marksmen kept following me, tracking me from place to place. Today I saw an elderly man, and fearing lest he were a hunter, I came up here in fright."

The tortoise said: "Don't be afraid, for we never see hunters around here at all. We offer you our affection, this spot of ours, and the pasture which is nearby."

The deer desired their companionship, and he settled down with them. They had an arbor nearby where they used to go every day. There they gathered and amused themselves by telling stories and chatting.

Then one certain day, the crow, the mouse, and the tortoise met in the arbor as was their wont, while the deer was absent.

They waited an hour for him, and as he was late in joining them, they got anxious lest some harm had befallen him. So they said to the crow: "Fly out to see if you notice the deer in anything like we suspect."

So the crow soared about and saw the deer in some hunter's snares, whereat he hurried away to inform the mouse and the tortoise about it.

The tortoise and the crow said to the mouse: "There is no hope except in you, so help our brother!"

The mouse scurried away till he came up to the deer, and said: "How did you fall into this scrape, when you are so nimble?"

The deer said: "What's the use of being nimble with hidden chances which can't be seen or guarded against?"

While they were discussing this, the tortoise appeared on the scene.

"The deer said to her: "You weren't right in coming to us, for if the hunter approaches and the mouse has finished cutting my ropes, I'll run away quickly, while the mouse has many caves and holes around here, and the crow will fly away. But you are awkward and that won't 'help$^{Sp)}$' you very much; so I'm afraid of what the hunter will do to you."

The tortoise said: "It is not considered living to be separated from one's dear ones; the help that comes both from consolation in the midst of worry and from heart's ease in affliction tells a friend when he has found a friend. One always shares his sorrow and complaints with friends, and when he is separated from their company, his vitals are wrenched, he is deprived of happiness, and the sparkle goes out of his eyes."

The tortoise had not finished speaking when the hunter came up. At that very moment, the mouse had gnawed through the ropes, and the deer escaped. The crow flew away, and the mouse went into a hole.

[D. The Tortoise a Captive]

When the hunter came up to his snare and saw it had been cut, he was surprised and began to look around. He did not see anything but the tortoise 'crawling along,' [η] so he seized her and tied her up with the ropes.

The deer, the crow, and the mouse soon gathered together and discovered that the hunter had taken the tortoise and tied her up. They were very sad at that, and the mouse said:

"We scarcely see ourselves through one tribulation, when we are beset with a harder one. The man was right who said: A man does not last very long without stumbling, and once he stumbles on soft soil, he keeps right on stumbling even when he is walking on firm ground.

"My luck was what separated me from family and wealth, from land and country, so it will 'not[Sp]' be pleased until it separates me from all those I have been living with, and from the company of the tortoise, the best of friends, whose friendship can neither be paid for nor sought in trade. Her friendship was noble and loyal, finer than a father's affection for his son, a friendship to end only with death. Woe on this body which is always experiencing misfortune and never stops changing and shifting!

"Nothing lasts or continues, just as a rising star does not keep on rising, nor a setting one keep setting, but they are continually changing places, the rising one always setting, and the setting one rising, the east turning west, and the west east. This grief recalls my [old] griefs, just as when a healed wound is hit again, its recipient experiences a two-fold pain: the pain of the blow, and the pain of reopening the wound. Similarly, one relives his hurts if he meets friends and then loses them."

The crow and the deer said to the mouse: "Our sadness and your sadness, and your words, no matter how eloquent they are, do not avail the tortoise one whit. So drop this and get busy looking for some escape for the tortoise, since it has been said: The courageous man is only tested in battle, the faithful person in mutual dealings, one's family and children in poverty, and friends in adversity."

The mouse said: "I see a means if you, o deer, will go off till you are near the huntsman's road and crouch down as if you were wounded and 'dying[Sp]'. The crow will swoop down on you as if he were getting ready to eat you, while I will follow close on the heels of the hunter; for I expect that if he catches sight of you, he will drop whatever he has like his bow and arrows and the tortoise, and hurry up to you.

"When he approaches you, hurry away from him, but dodging back and forth, so that he does not lose his desire of catching you. Make it seem easy for him from time to time, till he almost comes up to you; then lead him off a little further in whatever direction he can't overtake you. I on my side hope that the hunter will not return until I have finished cutting the rope binding the tortoise, when we will clear out with the tortoise and return home."

The deer did so, and the crow too. They worked along with each other, and were followed by the hunter a long while; then he went away. The mouse had meanwhile cut the tortoise' ropes, and they both escaped.

When the hunter came back, he found the rope cut and remembered the dodging deer and the crow pretending to eat him when he wasn't, and how his 'ropes'[n] had been gnawed in the first place. He felt very queer, and said: "What sort of land is this, but a land of witchcraft and a world of genii!"

So he turned his back upon it and went away, not looking for anything nor seeing it. The crow, the deer, the tortoise, and the mouse went off to their haunt safe and sound.

This is the tale of how friends
can help one another.

Here Ends the Chapter of the Ringdove.

Chapter IV

The Chapter

of the Owls and the Crows

[or War and Peace]

ING DABSHALIM said to Bidpai the philosopher: "You have just made me up a fable about true friends who help and love one another. Now if you see fit, make me up a story about the enemy whom one must not let deceive him, even though he seems to have a pleasant countenance and is deferential to you in public."

The philosopher said: "Whoever is deceived by a clever enemy who is known for his enmity, will be struck by what struck 'the owls because of' the crows."

The king said: "What was that?"

The philosopher said:

ONCE UPON A TIME IN A MOUNTAINOUS COUNTRY there was one of the largest trees in existence, which was thick with branches. In it were the nests of a thousand crows who had a king over them. On that mountain there was also a 'cave$^{Y/CeD)}$ with a thousand owls who had a king over themselves too. So the king of the owls came out one night because of the constant enmity between the owls and the crows, and he raided the crows with his owls, and killed and wounded many of them.

When it dawned, the king of the crows gathered his people together, and said to them: "You have seen what we have all suffered from the owls, and how this morning many of you are slain, or wounded, or with your head, wings, and tails plucked. Worse than all that for myself were their atrocities, for besides knowing your whereabouts, they attacked you boldly and energetically. So look carefully to your affair."

Now among them there were five crows recognized as outstanding in judgment, whom the crows relied upon and ran to whenever anything happened to them. Even the king consulted them in his administration, and accepted their advice.

So the king said to one of them: "What is your opinion in this matter?"

[1. Flight]

The crow said: "We have reached the opinion that there is no protection from an enraged foe whom cunning will not defeat, except in fleeing from him."

The king said to the second: "What is your opinion?

[2. See-saw]

He said: "I don't see that we should abandon our lands or our homes nor abase ourselves before our enemies at the first misfortune which befalls us. Rather we should get together in the matter and prepare to fight our enemy, setting lookouts between us and them, and guarding against a return of hostilities. If our enemies should advance upon us, we shall meet them prepared to kill, and we shall engage our cavalry against their cavalry. Let us protect ourselves by raising a fortress, so we may resist them for enough days till we find our chance; or if that is impossible, then we shall flee. 'Some time or other we shall seize an opportunity to do what we want and return the enemy our compliments[n].'"

The king said to the third: "And what is your opinion?"

[3. Vasallage]

He said: "I don't agree with what these two are saying, but I want you to set lookouts and scouts between us and our enemy. We shall thus find out for certain whether our enemy wants peace or will receive tribute from us. If we see that the matter is serious, I don't disapprove of making peace by offering them tribute. We shall thus avert their calamity from ourselves and live quietly at home. Indeed, one piece of advice for kings when their enemies' power increases and they fear the destruction and ruination of their land and their subjects' ruin, is to make their wealth into a shield for kings, lands, and subjects."

The king said to the fourth: "And what is your opinion about making peace?"

[4. Outright War]

He said: "I don't think so. Instead, leaving our homes and bearing up under exile and a hard life is better than surrendering our good name and humbling ourselves before an enemy when we are nobler and worthier than he. Nonetheless, I know that even if we offer them that, they will not consent to it except by misinterpreting it. Indeed it has been said: Offer your enemy some small token and you will get what you need; do not offer him everything you have, for the enemy will become bold towards you, your army will be weakened, and you yourself humiliated.

"That is like a board set up in the sun: if you let it lean over a little, its shadow will fall short.[1] Our enemy is not going to be pleased with the slightest token from us, and good sense tells us to make war on them and endure it."

The king said to the fifth: "What do you think about fighting, making peace, or emigrating?"

[5. War, But. . .]

He said: "As for giving battle, there is no way for anyone to fight when he 'has no strength$^{Y/CeD)}$ for it. Indeed it has been said: Whoever does not know himself and his enemy, and fights someone 'whom he cannot overpower, leads to his own demise$^\eta$. Besides, the intelligent man does not judge his enemy weak, for whoever does that is heedless, and whoever is heedless is unsafe. 'I am$^{Y/CeD)}$ in great awe of the owls, even though they give up fighting us, and I dreaded them even before they fell upon us.

"The clever man does not trust his enemy under any circumstances: if he is far away we do not trust his return; if he is close at hand, we do not trust his onset; if he is put to flight, we do not trust his guile. The shrewdest people are those who do not look for a means of fighting while a course is to be found elsewhere, because the outlay in fighting is first of all in lives, while other things can be paid for in money and words. You can't consider fighting the owls, for whoever thinks that everything rests on killing is 'bringing about his own death[η]'."

The king said: "Since you are loathe to fight, then what do you think?"

He said: "Go into consultation. If the king deliberates, he is more successful after consulting with intelligent persons than by using armies, troops, and abundance of materiel. Through deliberation, consultation, and his ministers' opinion, the wise king increases his wisdom as the sea increases through the affluence of the rivers. His own and his enemies' power is not hidden from the wise 'king[Ψ]', nor the time for fighting, and for decisions and stratagems.

"Neither does he neglect to go over matters personally one by one, and reflect where he should defer to his prospective allies' requirements, or to the equipment he must prepare for himself. Whoever has no such sense of judgment, nor acceptable counsel of intelligent ministers, will soon lose out even if fate drives happiness his way. For superiority is divided; it is not the lot of the ignorant nor yet of the well-born, but is granted to the intelligent man who lends an ear to those who are even more intelligent than he.

"And your majesty is like that, and some of what you have consulted me in, I want to answer secretly, and some publicly. What I don't mind disclosing here is that just as I do not advise fighting, likewise I do not advise humiliating ourselves by paying tribute and being pleased to submit to fate; for the intelligent, high-minded man prefers death while trying to defend himself, to life in shameful humility. I think you should not delay in probing into our affair, rather than shelving or overlooking it, for shelving and overlooking are the beginning of impotence.

"I prefer that secrets remain secrets, as they should; for it has been said: Kings do not achieve success except through wisdom; nor wisdom except through firm judgment; and judgment only by guarding secrets . . . [2] 'Secrets are revealed in five ways: through the lord; through his advisers[Ψ]; through messengers; through an eavesdropper, or whoever is approached by spies; or through one's own appearance and gestures. Whoever guards his secret will have the means of keeping it for two reasons: mastering what he wished; and saving himself from the danger and error of having committed a mistake.

"So it is, for no doubt the possessor of a secret consults a trustworthy man and unburdens his secrets to him so that he may help
him with his advice, even if the consultant is superior in judgment
to his adviser, for he thereby increases his own judgment just as fire
increases with fat and light. And an adviser ought to communicate
what he thinks in a straightforward manner to one who wants
advice, gradually bringing him to see and understand the mistake he
is committing and to change his mind insofar as he is off the track,
till they both agree upon the matter. When the counsellor is unlike
this, he is his consultant's enemy, just like the man who invokes the
devil to deal with some man, and if he is not skillful in how he does
it, the latter may clothe himself [in the former's body] and take
command of him.

"When a king is prudent with his secrets, consults his ministers,
and is held in proper respect by the common people, rarely letting
on what is on his mind nor neglecting to return a kindness in like
fashion, and does not make peace with the resolute man contrary to
fate, ʿrewards well one who does him a service, shuns whoever can
do him harm$^{Sp)}$ʾ, and is neither niggardly nor prodigal in his expenditures, that king should not be deprived of the dignity which has
been bestowed upon him.[3]

"ʿSecrets$^{Y/CeD)}$ʾ have degrees: some ʿsecrets$^{Y/CeD)}$ʾ one's kinsfolk
may share; some two men may share; and in some, one asks the
help of a faction. I do not see that this ʿsecret$^{Y/CeD)}$ʾ belongs anywhere
else than being shared with four ears and two tongues."

So the king stood up and went aside to consult with him.

It happened that ʿthe first thing$^{Y/CeD)}$ʾ he asked him was: "Do you
know the origin of the enmity between us and the owls?"

He said: "Yes; something a crow said."

The king said: "And what was that?"

The crow said:

[A. The Birds Choose A King]

"Once upon a time the nation of birds had no king, and they
agreed that an owl should be appointed to the post. While they were
at their meeting, a crow ʿappeared in the distance$^{Sp)}$ʾ, and some of
them said: 'Let's wait for this crow and ask his advice in the matter.'

"The crow came up to them, and they asked him his opinion.

"The crow said: 'If the birds became extinct, and the peacocks, the cranes, the ducks, and the doves all disappeared, would you feel compelled to stoop to making a king out of the owl, the ugliest bird to look at and known as the dirtiest? It has the least wits, the worst temper, and is the most unmerciful, besides having the drawback of being blind by day. And the worst of its defects is its indiscretion and bad manners.

" 'If you think$^{Y/CeD)}$ you should make him king, 'then run your own affairs^Y without his advice and decisions$^{Y/CeD)}$. That would be the same as the hares who said that the 'moon$^{Y/CeD)}$ was their king, and acted according to the opinion [they said] 'it sent them.^{ħ}'.'

"The birds said: 'How was that?'

"The crow said:

[A.1 The Elephants, the Hares, and the Moon]

Once upon a time the elephant's country suffered drought for years in succession. Water was scarce, its springs dried up, and a mighty thirst afflicted the elephants; so they complained of that to their king.

The king of the elephants sent his messengers and water-diviners to seek water everywhere, and one of his messengers returned and informed him that in such and such a place they had found a spring with plenty of water called the Moon Spring. So the king of the elephants went off with his elephants towards that spring in order to drink at it.

Now the country was the land of the hares, and the elephants drove the hares into their caves and haunts 'and many of them were killed$^{Y/CeD)}$. The hares gathered together before their king and said:

"You know what has been happening to us from the elephants. Think up something for us before they return; for if they come back to water, it means we'll be slaughtered!"

The king said: "Let every intelligent one among you offer his opinion."

One of the buckrabbits 'called Fayruz$^{Y/CeD)}$, whom the king knew for his fine breeding and good sense, came forward and said: "If the king sees fit to send me off to the elephants, along with a trusty person to see and hear what I saw, and then act so as to report to the king about it, then do so."

The king of the rabbits said: "You are my trusty man, and we are pleased with you and your opinion. We will believe whatever you say, so go off to the elephants and keep me informed about whatever you want. Do what you think best and know that through the messenger and his good sense one gets to know the intelligence of him who sends him and much more besides. Now you are smooth and conciliatory, and a messenger softens the heart when he acts smoothly, and hardens the breast when he is harsh."

So the buck went off on a night when there was a full moon, until he came near the elephants. He disliked going close to them, lest they would trample him even unintentionally; so he mounted a hill and called out:

"O king of the elephants, the Moon has sent me to you, and a messenger is not blamed even if he utters harsh words!"

The king of the elephants said: "What is your message?"

Fayruz said: "The Moon says: 'Whoever knows his superior strength over the weak, and thus rouses the jealousy of the strong, finds his strength is a defect. You know your superior strength over other beasts, and you thereby risked yourself with me: you come to my spring which is called after me, and you drink its water, and foul and disturb it with your elephants; while I order and warn you to go away or I shall smite you in the eyes and destroy you! If you are in any doubt about my message, then hie yourself to the spring at once, and I shall be there to meet you.' "

The king of the elephants wondered at Fayruz' speech, and he went off to the spring with him. He looked down at it, and saw the Moon's reflection.

Fayruz said to him: "Take some of the water in your trunk, wash your face, and bow down to the Moon."

When he put his trunk into the water, he disturbed it, so that the reflection was broken up and quivered. So he said to Fayruz:

"What is wrong with the 'Moon$^{Y/CeD}$ king? Don't you see he is angry with me for putting my trunk into the water?"

'Fayruz^{Y} the rabbit$^{Y/CeD}$ said: "Yes; so bow down to him."

So the elephant bowed down to the Moon, and repented for

what he had done to him. He agreed that neither he nor any of his elephants would return to that spring.

"The crow said: 'As for the matter of the owls, their affair means deceit, cunning, and guile. The worst of kings is the guileful, and whoever is afflicted with a guileful sovereign and lets him pass judgment, will have happen to him what happened to the quail and the rabbit, who let the fasting cat judge between them.'

"The 'birds^Y/CeD) said: 'And how was that?'

"The crow said:

[A.2 The Quail, the Rabbit, and the Cat]

I once had a 'neighbor^Y/CeD) at the foot of a mountain who was a quail. His covert was by a tree where I had my nest, so we often used to meet, and struck up a close friendship through being neighbors.

Then I lost track of him, and did not know where he had gone. He was away so long in fact, that I thought he had perished. A rabbit came to the quail's place without my knowledge, and the rabbit abode in that spot for quite a while. Then the quail returned home.

When he found the rabbit in it, he said: "This is my place, so clear out!"

The rabbit said: "I am living here, while you are only asking for it. If you are in the right, then request it politely."

The quail said: "The place is mine, and I can prove it!"

The rabbit said: "We need a judge then."

The quail said: "Near us on the seashore there lives a devout cat who prays all day long. He does not harm any animal nor shed any blood, and he fasts all the while without a break. He just lives off water and grass. So let's go to him at night, so he can pass judgment for you."

The rabbit said: "Yes."

So they both went off together, and I followed them to see how he would keep his fast and judge between them.

'When the cat saw the rabbit and the quail in the distance, he stood up to pray^Y/CeD and to display his humility and devotion. They both^Y marveled when they saw^Y/CeD his goodness and humility. They approached him^ℑ), and when they were with the cat, they related their story to him.

The cat said: "Age is drawing on me, and my ears are getting dull, so that I can scarcely hear. Come nearer so you can tell me at close range!"

So they both repeated their story, and he said: "I understand what you two have said. Now I want to give you some advice before the decision, urging you to claim only what is your due. Whoever seeks his right will be successful 'even though the decision goes against him[Y/CeD]', whereas if the judgment is for him while he is making a false claim, he is 'beaten[Y/CeD]'. The worldly man has nothing such as wealth or friends, but only his own good works.

"Now the intelligent person is right in endeavoring to seek what will remain with him and whose advantage will return to him 'in the next world[Sp]', and he hates things other than that. To the intelligent man, the dignity of wealth is the dignity of dried mud; the women one has no right to are on the same level as vipers; and the dignity of men who love good and loathe evil is the same as one's own."

He continued 'preaching to[Sp]' and treating them amiably, so that they came close up to him. Then he leaped upon them, and seized and killed them both.

"The crow said: 'The owl combines what I have described to you: craft and guile. Don't make the owl your king, as you are proposing!'

"So the birds heeded what the crow urged upon them, and they did not make the owl their king.

"Then the owl said to the crow: 'You have avenged yourself upon me in a hard way. I don't know whether some evil has befallen you because of me, for me to deserve this from you. If not, you know that a tree can be cut with an axe and it will sprout again; the sword can be used to cut flesh and bone, and it is healed and mended; while the tongue's wound never heals. An arrow's barb can be buried in the abdomen and then pulled out, whereas the barbs of talking cannot be pulled out nor withdrawn once they reach the heart. Any conflagration is extinguished as fire is by water, poison by an antidote, passion by 'separation[Y/CeD]', and sadness by long-suffering; while the fire of rancor is never extinguished. You tribe of crows have certainly planted a tree of rancor between us for all time!'

"The owl made this speech angrily, and he went away looking for vengeance.

"The crow regretted having acted so hastily towards him, and he said to himself: 'I certainly have been foolish in what I said, for it has won hatred for me and my people. I was not the best bird to talk like this, nor the most suitable to discuss who should be king. Perhaps many saw just what I saw, and knew what I knew, and kept from talking for fear of what I did not fear and foreseeing consequences I did not notice.

" 'This applies especially since the talking was done face to face, for in talks where both the speaker and the listener are present, it is disagreeable when rancor and malice spring up; it should not be called talk, but rather poisoning. Indeed even if the intelligent man is confident of his 'strength*$^{Y/CeD}$* and superiority, he is not obliged to bring enmity and hatred down upon himself by relying upon his judgment and strength. It is like an intelligent man who does not drink poison, even though he has an antidote he can rely upon.

" 'The merit of well-doers lies in doing and 'not in saying; for if*^{Sp}* by some accident, 'the doer falls short on what he says*^{Sp}*', his merit stands out through experience and his past dealing; while even if the fluent talker has a wonderful way of describing things, his treatment does not turn out to be praiseworthy. 'I am*$^{Y/CeD}$* a talkative individual who does not end up 'praiseworthy*^{y}*', and my indiscretion lies in daring to speak about an important matter without consulting anyone and turning it over and over in my mind. I know that whoever does not consult keen-witted advisers repeatedly, is not happy at how his judgment turns out; so what is my excuse in what I have fallen into today?'

"The crow chided himself in this way, and then he went away.

"This is the cause of the enmity between the owls and the crows which you asked me about."

The king said: "Indeed, I have understood this; so tell me what we must do. Give me your opinion about what you think we should do in the affair between us and the owls."

He said: "I have exhausted my opinion about fighting, and let you know my disapproval of it. I hope I can contrive some way out 'if God the All-Highest so wills it*^{y}*', for He is the Lord of Men. Indeed they have used knavish tricks in a serious matter in order to gain what they needed, when they could not have accomplished it with numbers; just as the gang deceived the ascetic and took away his kid."

The king said: "How was that?"

'The crow⁽ˢᵖ⁾ said:

[B. The Monk and the Kid]

"Once upon a time an ascetic bought a fat, plump kid for a sacrifice. He went off leading it 'by a rope⁽ˢᵖ⁾. A gang of sharpers saw him, and they consulted about tricking him.

"'So they went along the road he would have to follow⁽ˢᵖ⁾, and one of them stopped in front of him and said: 'O monk, what is this dog with you?'

"Then another stopped in front of him and said: 'O monk! I suppose you want to go hunting with this dog?'

"Then still another stopped before him and said: 'Really, I think this man with ascetic's clothes on is not one, since an ascetic never leads a dog!'

"So he said: 'Perhaps whatever they sold me has charmed my 'eyes⁽ʳ⁾.'

"Then he set the kid loose and abandoned it; and the gang took it and shared it amongst themselves.

"I have only made you up this story since I expect to attain our needs through 'deceit and ⁽ˢᵖ⁾ cunning. I think the king should become angry with me and order me brought before the chiefs of his army and beaten and pecked until I am covered with blood. Then pluck out my feathers and tail, and cast me at the foot of a tree. The king and his attendants should then ride off to such and such a spot till I contrive some trick. Then I shall come to inform you of what I have done."

So that was done, and the king rode off with his crows to the spot indicated by him. Then the owls came by night and did not find the crows. Nor did they notice the crow at the foot of the tree.

He was anxious lest they go away before they saw him, so that his torment would be in vain; so he started to moan and to groan till some of the owls heard him. When they saw him, they informed their king about him, and he proceeded to him with some owls to ask about the crows. As they drew near him, he ordered an owl to ask him who he was and where were the crows.

The crow said: "I am So-and-so, son of So-and -so. Concerning what you ask me about the crows, I don't reckon you see me in any condition to know any secrets."

The owl king said: "This is the king of the crows' minister and privy counsellor! Ask him what sort of offence he committed to have this done to him."

The crow said: "They thought my advice was silly, and did this to me."

The king said: "What was this silly thing?"

The crow said: "When you descended upon us, our king asked us our advice, saying: 'O crows, what do you think?'

"I was there at the time, so I said: 'I think you have no power to fight the owls, for they are more violent and bolder than you. But good sense lies in two directions: we may seek peace; and we may offer tribute. They will accept that from you; otherwise you must flee the country.'

"I informed the crows that fighting was better for you and worse for them, and that peace was the most favorable condition they could obtain from you. I ordered them to surrender, and made up a simile for them about that, saying: 'A strong enemy is not diverted from a bold attack and anger in any better way than by surrendering to him. Don't you see that grass is not safe from a gusty wind except by yielding and bending whichever way it turns?'

"They got angry at what I said, and claimed they wanted to fight; and then they became suspicious of me and said: 'No!' They rejected my advice and good counsel and punished me in this fashion."

When the king of the owls heard what the crow said, he remarked to one of his ministers: "What do you think of this crow?"

The latter said: "Don't look any further than killing him off, for this individual is one of the crows' most advanced weapons, and by killing him we shall hive a mighty victory[4] and a respite from his advice and artfulness. Besides, his loss to the crows will be great.

"It has been said: Whoever has the chance to settle a serious

matter and misses it, is unable to come by it a second time;
whoever seeks an opening for a stroke and lets it slip, then his
stroke falls amiss and his opportunity never returns; and whoever
finds a weak and destitute enemy and does not get rid of him, is
struck by regret just when his enemy is gaining ground and preparing for action, and he is not a match for him."

The king said to another of his ministers: "What do you think
of this crow?"

He said: "I think you should not kill him, since a lowly, defence-
less enemy ought to be shown mercy, let live, and pardoned. The
timorous man who asks help ought to be trusted and aided, since a
man is often won over to his enemy through some slight favor,
like the thief who made the merchant's wife act kindly toward him
without intending to."

The king said: "How was that?"

The minister said:

[C. The thief and the Merchant's Wife]

"Once upon a time a wealthy old merchant, who was still not
too repulsive, had a young and beautiful wife. He was madly in
love with her, while she loathed him and did not let him touch her,
no matter how much he needed to. Meanwhile the merchant
learned what was on her mind, and that merely increased his love
for her.

"Then a thief came to the merchant's house by night. When he
entered the house, he found the merchant sleeping while his wife
was awake. She was startled by the thief, and jumped upon the
merchant and held on to him.

"The merchant awoke, grasped her, and said: 'Whence this
favor?'

"When he noticed the thief, and realized what had induced his
wife was [her desire] to be rid of the thief, he called out to him:

'O thief, you may have whatever you like! Take my wealth and
belongings, since you have been so kind as to make this woman
care enough for me to embrace me!' "

Then the king asked the third of his ministers about the crow.
He said: "I consider you should let him live and treat him

kindly, since he must be able to give you some good advice. Indeed, the intelligent man considers it a fine stroke to stir up strife amongst his enemies, because some enemies are worried about others, and a disagreement amongst them brings a respite, like the relief the ascetic found when the robber and the devil disagreed."

The king said: "And how was that?"

The minister said:

[D. The Robber, the Devil, and the Hermit]

"Once upon a time an ascetic received a milch cow from a 'noble[Sp)] man. He went away, leading her to his dwelling, while a robber followed him, wanting to steal her. Then a devil in the shape of a man made friends with him.

"So the robber said to the devil: 'Who are you?'

"He said: 'I am a devil wanting to follow this ascetic. When people are asleep, I shall seize and strangle him.'

The robber said: 'And I want to follow him home so I may steal his cow.'

"So they both went off as good friends until they came close to the ascetic's dwelling, just as evening was drawing on. The ascetic entered his home and made the cow come into the house. Then he had supper and went to sleep.

"The robber became anxious lest the devil should begin by seizing the ascetic before he had secured the cow, so that the ascetic would cry out and people would gather at the sound of his voice, and he could not steal the bovine.

"So he said to him: 'You watch while I get the cow out; then you take on the man.'

"The devil was meanwhile anxious lest the robber would start something that someone would notice and therefore waken the ascetic, and he would not be able to seize him.

"So he said: 'You wait for me to seize the monk, and then you can attend to the cow.'

"Each of them refused his friend, and they did not stop arguing until the robber called out to the ascetic in this fashion: 'Wake up, monk, for this devil wants to catch you!'

"The devil called out to him too: 'Wake up, you ascetic, for this robber wants to take your cow!'

"At both their voices, the monk was roused as well as his neighbors, and he escaped them. Neither could do as he wanted, and both trouble-makers fled disappointed."

When the third finished his speech, the first who had advised killing the crow said:

"I see that this crow has deceived and beguiled you with his speech and humble manner. You [others] are ruining common sense and misinterpreting a serious matter, so that little by little 'your majesty'[n] will hold this same opinion.

"Pay attention to sensible persons who know their own and others' business, and don't be turned aside and act like those ineffectuals who are fooled into believing that what they hear is more worthy of credence than what they know. That is like the carpenter who took for a lie what he saw and knew, and took for true what he only heard, so that he was deceived and fooled."

The king said: "And how was that?"

The minister said:

[E. The Carpenter Who Let His Wife Two-Time Him]

"Once upon a time a carpenter had a wife whom he loved. Now there was a man who hung around her, and some of the caprenter's people got wind of that and informed him.

"The carpenter wished to make certain of it, and so he said to his wife: 'I want to go to a village some leagues away on some government work. I'll be staying there some days, so get me some provisions ready.'

"The woman was glad at that, and arranged some provisions for him. When it came evening, he said to her:

" 'Lock your house door and stay at home until I return some days from now!'

"He went out, and she watched till he had passed out the door 'and gone a good distance[P]'. Then he turned back 'another way[P]', and entered the woman's house. He went into her bedroom and crawled under the bed.

"Now the woman had told her sweetheart: 'Come along, for the carpenter has gone off on some business and will be absent for some days.'

"So the man came to her, and she gave him food and drink. Then he went to bed with her, and they both dallied away at their game for a long while until drowsiness overcame the carpenter. He fell asleep, and his two legs slipped out from under the bed.

"The woman saw them, and realized that her bad habits had been discovered. So, letting the man in on her secret, she said:

" 'Raise your voice and ask me if I like my husband!'

"The Man asked her: 'Do you like your husband?' just as she said.

"She rebuffed him: 'Oh, my darling, don't force me to answer such a question! Don't you know that we women generally want sweethearts just to fulfill our urge and not because they are handsome or because of their characters, nor for anything like that? Once we have satisfied our need with one of them, he is like any other stranger; while a husband is just like a brother and children. May God curse the woman whose husband is not a part of herself! I won't hear you mention it another time!'

"When the carpenter heard what his wife had said, he felt sorry for her, and weeping and pity for her gripped him. He was fortified to think that she was fond of him, and he took an aversion to harming her. Thus he did not leave his place until it dawned, and he knew that the sweetheart had left. He came out from under the bed, and found his wife sleeping.

"So he sat down at her head and began to watch over her until she commenced to stir. As she was waking up, he said:

" 'My darling love, slumber on, since you are so worn out from loss of sleep! If it were not that I hated doing evil, there would have been a row that would really have amounted to something between me and that man!'

"I have only told you this fable because I didn't want you to be like that carpenter who belied his sight and believed what he heard from his wife. Don't put credence in what the crow says; remember that many enemies are incapable of harming their foes at a distance, and try to get close and pull the wool over their eyes. I don't fear the crows at all; my fear has arisen since I have seen this crow and heard what you are saying about him."

The king of the owls and the rest of his ministers did not listen to his words. [Instead] the owl king ordered the crow brought home with them, and he granted him wealth and honor.

So the minister who had advised killing him said: "When this crow was not killed, he then assumed the rank of an enemy who is feared for his evil and should be guarded against. The crow is a past master of cunning and wiles, and I do not consider he took refuge with us except for his own good and our ruin."

The king did not raise his head at this speech, nor stop honoring and treating the crow kindly. The latter began to talk as affably as he could whenever [the king] entered his quarters, and when he was alone with the owls, he spoke words which increased their confidence in him daily. So they became familiar and polite, and began to trust him.

Then one day when a group of owls were with him, and amongst them the owl who had advised killing him, he said:

"Will some of you tell the king on my behalf, that since the crows hate me so and have disgraced and punished me, my heart will never be at peace until I attain my will of them. I have pondered and find I can do nothing since I am a crow. However, I have learned from one of the king's people that whoever wants to better himself, should allow himself to be consumed by fire. Thus he comes extremely close to God, and he will not make any request of Him without His granting it.

"Therefore, if the king sees fit to command me thus, let him have me burnt so I can beg my Lord to change me into an owl. Then when I have taken on an owl's shape, I can avenge myself of my enemies and quench my thirst for revenge."

The owl who had advised killing him said: "Nothing resembles you in your fine front and your evil insides, except wine with a good bouquet and a beautiful color where poison is lurking. Do you think your essence and nature would change if we burnt you in a fire? It would not! You would return to whatever you came from, and revert to your origin and nature, like the rat who found she could have the sun, the clouds, the wind, and the mountain as husbands, and still left all that to marry a rat."

He was asked: "And how was that?"

The owl said:

[F. The Rat Girl]

"Once upon a time there lived a pious ascetic whose prayers were usually answered. Once while he was sitting on a river bank, a hawk passed by with a young rat in its claws. It dropped it near the ascetic, so pity overcame him and he took it up and wrapped it in ⁽a leaf$^{Y/CeD)}$, intending to take it home with him. Then he was afraid it would be hard for his family to bring up, so he called upon his Lord[5] to change it into a girl.

"So He ⁽changed her and$^{Y/CeD)}$ granted her beauty and charm. The ascetic went off home with her and said to his wife: 'This is my daughter, so act towards her as you would towards a child of your own.'

"She did so until she reached twelve years of age, when he said to her: 'O daughter, you have come of age now, and must have a husband; so choose someone you love from among men and genii and marry him.'

"She said: 'I want a strong and powerful husband.'

"So he said: 'Perhaps you want the sun, ⁽who is very noble and powerful, higher than everything in the world. I want to pray to him and ask him to do you the favor of marrying you$^{Sp)}$.'

"So he ⁽performed his ablutions and$^{Sp)}$ said to the sun: ⁽'O mighty creature$^{Y/CeD)}$, this charming girl lives at home with me on the same footing as one of our own children. Now I am marrying her to you, since she is looking for a strong and irresistible husband.'

"The sun said: 'I shall point out something more powerful than I: the cloud which conceals my light and overpowers it.'

"So the monk went off to ⁽where the clouds come in from the sea$^{Sp)}$ and said the same to it as he had said before.

"The cloud said to him: 'I shall point out someone to you who is stronger and more powerful than I: the wind which blows me to and fro.'

"So the hermit went off to the wind and said the same to him as he had said elsewhere.

"The wind said: 'I'll show you someone who is more powerful than I: the mountain whom I am powerless to move.'

"So the ascetic went off to the mountain and asked it the same as before.

"The mountain said: 'I shall point out someone who is more powerful than I: the rat who bores through me, while I am unable to do anything about him.'

"The hermit 'went off and $^{Y/C^cD)}$ said to the rat: 'Do you want to marry this girl?' .

"He said to him: 'How can I marry her while I am small and my burrow is so narrow?'

"So the girl besought the hermit to pray to his Lord on her behalf, to change her into a rat. He consented, and prayed to his Lord. The latter changed her back into a rat, and the male rat married her. Thus she returned to her original state.

"This is like you, you deceiver!"

Neither the king of the owls nor any of his attendants paid any attention to this speech. They kept on visiting the crow and cared for nothing except honoring him, until he was on very good terms with them. His feathers came back in, and he grew plump and healthy. He found out what he wanted to know, and made a study of everything he desired.

Then he stole back to the crows and said to the crow king: "I have good news for you concerning my success in 'killing the owls$^{\wp)}$'. You need only take the offensive, for if you exert yourselves and carry this business through, it means the end of the owl king and his army!"

The king of the crows said: "We are at your service, so order us to do whatever seems proper."

The crow said: "The owls live at such and such a place, and by day they gather in such and such a 'cave$^{\wp)}$ in the mountain. Now I have found a place where there is much dry kindling, so let each of your crows carry what he can of that wood to the mouth of the cave where the owls stay during the day.

"Then near that mountain is a flock of sheep, and I shall go over and get fire from it. I'll bring it to the door of the 'cave$^{\wp)}$ and toss it in upon the wood which has been collected. Then you will shout and keep flapping your wings to fan the flame till the wood catches. Whatever owls come out will be burned in the fire, and whatever remain will die in the smoke."

They did so, and killed the owls. Then they returned to their homes safe and sound.

Later the king of the crows asked that crow: "How did you stand the owls' company, for good men cannot stand the company of evil men?"

The crow said: "That is indeed so; but when some weighty and difficult affair befalls an intelligent man, wherein he fears a devastating calamity for himself and his people, he will display the greatest patience when he has some hope of success. He does not consider it mad nor 'despicable ⁿ' to humiliate himself towards his inferiors until he gains what he needs; [rather] he rejoices at a chance to put an end to things, with the satisfaction that it is through his judgment and long-suffering."

The king said: "Tell me how intelligent the owls are."

The crow said: "I didn't find an intelligent one among them, except the owl who urged them to kill me. The rest were weak-minded and did not see into my affair. They forgot that I had been a person of standing with the crows, and am reputed to have good judgment, nor were they afraid of any cunning or guile.

"Now that straight-forward adviser who realized what was on my mind, offered them his opinion and advised them soundly; but they rejected his advice, for they had no intelligence nor would they receive any. They neither took precautions nor concealed their secrets from me."

He said [further]: "A king should conceal his personal secrets from any suspicious individual and not even think of letting him handle his secrets and correspondence, nor his water and wash-basin, nor his bed, clothing, and suits, nor his steed and weapons, nor his food, drink and medicine, nor his gold, scents and herbs."

The king of the crows said: "The owl king did not perish because of me but through his own shortcomings and his ministers' bad judgment."

The crow said: "It has been truly said: Few conquer anyone with[out] injustice;⁶ few 'hanker for ^Y/CᶜD' women without being put to shame; few eat too much without becoming ill; and few are afflicted with evil ministers who do not fall into destruction. And it has been said: Does not a pompous man feed on high-sounding praise; a rascal on his many friends; a boor on fairplay; a stingy individual on bounty; a greedy⁷ man on his few faults; and a shifty, comtemptible king with poor ministers on the stability of his kingdom?"

The king of the crows said: "You endured mighty tribulation in dwelling with the owls and humbling yourself towards them."

The crow said: "It was bound to be that way; but I endured it for what I hoped to accomplish. For it has been said: It is nothing extraordinary for a man to carry his enemy upon his shoulders, when he is confident of achieving his downfall. Indeed it has been said: Whoever endures difficulty hopes for some advantage, enduring it as the snake suffered carrying the frog on its back."

The king said: "How was that?"

The crow said:

[G. The Snake and the Frog-King]

"Once upon a time a snake grew old and weak, and was no longer able to go hunting. He could not obtain food, so he crawled along searching woefully and wistfully until he came to a pool of water full of frogs. He had been accustomed to come and hunt the frogs in it, so he collapsed near the pool as if he were sad and distraught.

"Now a frog happened to say to him: 'What's wrong with you? I see you are sad.'

"He said 'I can't help being sad with what I have, for I had a better living when I was hunting frogs; and if I happen upon any now, I dare not eat them.'

"So the frog went off to his king with the news he had heard about the snake.

"The king approached the snake and said to him: 'How have you reached this state?'

"The snake said: 'I am unable to accept any frogs excepting whatever the king may give me as alms.'

"He said: 'Why?'

"He said: 'A few nights ago I was busy on the trail of a frog, trying to catch it, and I followed it to an ascetic's darkened house. It went in, and I entered on its trail. In the house was the ascetic's son, and I caught his finger, thinking it was the frog. I stung it and he died. So I fled outside with the ascetic after me.

" 'He called to me and said: "Why did you kill the innocent boy wrongfully? I call down humiliation and disgrace upon you! You shall become a mount for the king of the frogs, while frogs are forbidden you! You will not be able to eat any except what their king may give you as alms."

" 'So I have come for you to ride me whenever you feel so inclined.'

"Now the king of the frogs had longed to ride a snake, and he thought that would be an honor and a dignity for him. So he rode the snake for some days.

"Then the snake said to him: 'You know that I am accursed and outlawed, and cannot catch anything except what you give me as alms. So make me some gift I may live off.'

"The king said: 'Upon my life, since you're my steed, I can't help granting you a living.'

"So he ordered two frogs for him every day. They were both caught and delivered to him, and he lived off that. His pride was not injured for having a contemptible enemy, since he derived benefit and a free living from it.

"Likewise I endured what I did in search of this great boon which helped ruin our enemies and make peace with them."

The king said: "I have found that a meek and cunning man is more successful in uprooting an enemy than a man of strong action, for fire does not attack a tree fiercely unless it is dried up on the ground, while water uproots what is underground with its meekness and coldness. It has been said: Four things are not to be belittled for being small; fire, illness, an enemy, and a debt."

The crow said: "Whatever happened was through the king's good fortune and judgment, for it has been said that when two men seek happiness, the manlier achieves it, while if they are equally manly, then the keener-witted of them. And if they are equals in this, then the one with more helpers; and if they are equal in that, then the luckier.

"For it has been said: Whoever 'fights$^{Y/CeD)}$ a wise, clever king with willing allies who is neither giddy in happiness nor bewildered when hurt, 'is calling down his own destruction$^{Y/CeD)}$; especially when he is like your majesty, who knows government and the time for action, the place for violence and meekness, anger and pleasure, speed and delay, and who looks into his present ʿand future$^{Y/CeD)}$ and follows up their consequences."

The king said: "It was rather your judgment and intelligence that gave one man victory over an enemy with many military supplies as well as men. Indeed so far as I am concerned, the most surprising part of your business is how long you stayed with the owls, hearing their coarse talk and seeing the same sort of conduct, and then never letting a word slip out while you were with them!"

The crow said? "I couldn't help profiting from your good example, your majesty, by making friends of the kinsfolk and stranger with compassion and gentleness, and following, heeding, and obeying them. It has been said: Whoever has dealings with an enemy, and wants to harm and ruin him, should place meekness and obedience ahead of his own inclinations."

The king said: "I find you speak sane words, except that you had no assistance against them."

The crow said: "It has been said that when the perfect man asks advice of persons with superior judgment and intelligence, at the beginning he sees and hears disparaging remarks which go against the grain and yet result to his advantage and in peace and happiness; while if advice merely follows the consultant's whim and does not consider consequences, even though it may render fleeting joy and peace, still the matter will result in harm and loss."

The king said: "I find you are a master workman, while other ministers are master speech-makers who never produce any results. The same goes for the king's friends. Indeed ʿin you$^{ｬ)}$ God has bestowed a mighty favor upon us, and we could not find any pleasure in eating, drinking, or sleeping until ʿyou returned$^{ｬ)}$."

The crow said:[8] "It has indeed been said: The sick man does not enjoy sleeping or eating, until he is cured; nor the greedy man whom a king has enticed with wealth and a post, until he attains it; nor the man who is harassed by an enemy whom he fears night and day, until he is relieved of him. It is also said: Whomever a fever quits has his heart relieved; whoever puts down a heavy burden, has his back relieved; and whoever dares to trust his enemy, can breathe a sigh of relief.

"And I pray ʿGod$^{Y/CeD)}$, who slew your enemies, to maintain you in power and that He grant this for our subjects' welfare and happiness. May He make them happy that you are reigning, for if a king's subjects have no joy, then his kingdom is like the wattles on a goat which a ⸢kid⸣ hunts [as a teat] and does not find provide any sustenance."[9]

The king said: "What was the owl king's way with his courtiers?"

He said: "His way was scornful, scoffing, deceitful, lazy, and short-sighted. All his companions and ministers were the same, except the one who advised killing me."

He said: "Why do you think he showed such good sense towards you?"

He said: "He had two qualities: his opinion was to kill me, which advice he did not conceal even when his master made light of it; and his words were not stupid and haughty, but gentle and mild, so that often he told him his faults without his getting angry with him. He merely made up stories telling him about other people's faults in such a way that he could see his own and still not get angry with him.

"Once I heard him telling the king: 'Your majesty should not ignore ⸢the crow's⸣ affair, for it is an important piece of business which can only be tackled by a few. You must face it resolutely, for if it slips by, there is no overtaking it. If the king is steadfast and acts energetically, he should be victorious and mighty. Whoever does not handle his government and subjects well, will have little peace and quiet, like a monkey running back and forth in a hurry and a flurry.

" 'A kingdom is a serious and eminent acquisition, and whoever conquers one should see carefully to its trust and defence. For it has been said: Whoever is fickle is just as unstable as a streak ⸢of water⸣ on a waterlily leaf; if on the alert, like a python; in his coming and going, like the wind; if he weighs you down, like the company of someone you loathe;[10] in being as fearful as a devastating catastrophe, like the snake; in leaving quickly, like water after a rainfall; and in his ingratitude, like envy. Whatever he offers is like dreaming of ⸢riches⸣ in one's sleep: when one awakes, nothing can be found of the dream.'

"So may God cause the king's enemies to perish, and make him to prevail over them! May his majesty, achievement, and succour never cease!"

Thus Ends the Chapter of the Owls and the Crows.

Chapter V

The Chapter of
the Monkey and the Tortoise[1]
[Or Butterfingers]

HE KING said to the philosopher: "I have heard the story of the man who was deceived by his enemy, and how a smart man pretending to be humble and flattering only wanted to fool and deceive him, and what followed. Now if you see fit, make me up a story about a man who seeks what he needs and then loses it just as he has it within his grasp.'

The philosopher said: "Attaining your needs is easier than retaining them. Whoever gains his point and is unable to maintain it, loses what he has acquired, like the tortoise who sought the monkey's heart, and lost it just when he had it in his power."

The king said: "How was that?"

The philosopher said:

ONCE UPON A TIME a band of monkeys had a king called Qaradin. He had lived so long that old age finally wore him out. One of the youthful monkeys raised a faction against him, and said: "This fellow has grown doddery and is incapable and unfit to reign."

His followers fell in with him, and they banished the aged thing from their kingdom, setting up the youth as king in his stead. So the aged one went off till he reached the coast, where he came upon a fig tree planted by the seashore. He started eating some of its figs, and one fell out of his hand into the water. A tortoise or male turtle was in the way of the fig, and he picked it up and ate it.

When the monkey heard the fig falling in the water, he was surprised. In fact, he took a fancy to the noise of the fig falling into the water and 'never ate without repeating the experiment[Kn)]. The tortoise began to pick them up and eat them, not doubting that the monkey was flinging those figs for his sake.

So the tortoise came out to meet the monkey, and they both shook hands and struck up a real friendship. They lived together and each of them got along very well with the other. Thus they sojourned for a while, and the tortoise did not return to his people.

The tortoise' wife meanwhile was sad at her spouse's absence, and complained of that to a neighbor of hers, saying: "I'm afraid that some bad accident has happened to him!"

Her friend said to her: "Don't be sad, for I have learned that your husband is on the seashore with a monkey. He has made friends with him, and they both are eating and drinking together and idolizing each other. This is why he has been absent for such a long time; so forget about him as he does not care the same for you as you do for him. Yet if you're able to find some way of killing the monkey, then do so; for if the monkey is killed, then your husband will stay at home with you."

Now the tortoise' wife lost color and wasted away till she became very exhausted and emaciated.

After a while the tortoise said: "I am fond of my people and have been away a long time."

So he went off home and found his wife in a bad state. He said: "O love, how are? Why do I see you so worn out?"

She did not answer, so he asked her again and her neighbor replied for her, saying:

"Your wife is in serious condition; her illness is critical and its remedy is not to be found. What else is there except her death, considering the seriousness of the disease and the lack of medicine?"

The husband said: "Now tell me about the remedy, and perhaps I can find out where some is."

She said: "This sickness is known to us [she-]tortoises,[2] and there is no remedy for it except to get a monkey's heart and prepare it."

The tortoise said to himself: "This is a difficult matter. Where else can I get a monkey's 'heart^{Ⴥ)} except my friend's? Either I betray my friend, or else my wife perishes; and all of this leaves me no defence."

Then he added: "When a man is unable to accomplish anything great except by overlooking something small, he should not heed the small thing; and one's wife's right is great and she is useful and helpful in this world and the next. I am therefore correct in making things easy for her and not neglecting her rights."

Then he returned to the monkey with this problem on his mind. He was muttering and saying: "Indeed, my killing a trusting and close friend for slight cause is a matter that is liable to turn out quite terribly!"

He turned that over and over in his mind until he came to the monkey. He wished him well, and said to him:

"When you were deprived of me, O brother, how did it afflict you?"

The tortoise answered: "It was not so much being afflicted with yearning for you, 'but rather'' shyness and bashfulness that I had rewarded you so little for your kindness during your misfortune of being with me and your services towards me. Indeed I know that you are not asking me for any recompense for your services; but I still want to reward you, for I ought to. You have the same character as those noble people who do good to someone who has not done so to them in the past, and do not expect to in the future: they do not bring up any service they have performed nor ask too much in the way of reward, and they freely help the needy."

The monkey said: "Don't speak this way nor spare me, for you established these things between us, starting with whatever requital is necessary, and granting what you saw fit. Didn't I arrive despised by my nation, expelled, exiled, and alone; and you were a comfort and a companion unto me? Through you, God removed my anxiety and grief!"

The tortoise said: "There are three things which increase the kindness and familiarity shown by friends, none of which occurred between you and me, much as I would have like it: one of them is frequenting a man's house; another, seeing 'his ^{Ⴥ)} people and family; and another, eating together."

The monkey said: "A friend ought to seek the essence of himself in his friend. As for seeing 'his^{Ⴥ)} people and family, a player[3] on a musical instrument sees many people's folks and family; as for eating together, horses, mules, and donkeys all get together to eat; and as for a man entering a [house], a thief enters the place of a man he knows. Players do not become friendlier with people through seeing them and their household, nor beasts on getting together to eat, nor robbers with the acquaintances they make by entering men's homes."

The tortoise said: "Upon my word, you are right; for a friend does not seek anything of a friend except his affection. He who seeks worldly advantages ought to be cut off from his brethren, for it has been said: A man never burdens his brethren with tribulations till he injures and wearies them, like the cow's calf who sucks her so much that she finally drives him away in a hurry 'with her horn$^{Sp)}$. I haven't mentioned this except that I am aware of your natural generosity and liberality. But I would love you to visit me at home; I live on an island with many fine fruit trees. Please give in and ride home on my back!"

The monkey was eager at the mention of the fruit, and he agreed to the tortoise' request. He jumped on his back, and the tortoise swam with him until he was in midstream. Then it entered his mind what an ugly deed he was contemplating, and how wicked and treacherous it was.

He stopped and pondered, saying to himself: "The thing I am planning is ungrateful and treacherous. Females are not people for whom one should yield to treachery and villainy, for they are not to be trusted not treated kindly. It has been said: Gold is known in fire, a man's loyalty by give and take, the strength of animals by their load; while women have nothing by which they are known."

When the monkey saw the tortoise was stopping instead of swimming, he became suspicious and said to himself: "What is making the tortoise stop, unless it is to think something over: How can I be sure about how his heart is? He has altered and changed towards me, and 'wants to do me$^{Sp)}$ a bad turn!

"I have learned there is nothing hastier than the heart, nor quicker to change and to alter. The intelligent man does not fail to find out what is on his family's, children's, brethren's, or friends' mind in every matter and through every glance and word, in how they stand up and how they sit down, and through every state they are in. All that bears witness to what is in their hearts."

Then he said to the tortoise: "What is holding you back, and why do I see you are worried?"

He said: "It worries me that you are going to my home, and will not find everything as you desire, since my wife is seriously ill."

The monkey said: "Don't worry, for worry satisfies nothing. Look for medicines and physicians for your wife, since it has been said: The wealthy man bestows his riches in three places; in charity if he wants a reward in the other world; in works for his ruler if he wants rank in this world; and in woman if he wants comfort in living."[4]

The tortoise said: "The doctors say there is no medicine for her except a monkey's heart."

The monkey said to himself: "How wrong I have been! Greed has hurled me into one of the worst holes for old age! He spoke rightly who said: The temperate, contented man lives safely, quietly, restfully, and cheerfully; while the greedy glutton lives out his life in weariness, toil, and fear. I must use my wits to seek a way out of what I have fallen into!"

So he said to the tortoise: "When you knew this, my friend, what kept you from telling me so that I might bring my heart along with me?"

He said: "Why, where is your heart?"

He said: "I left it behind at my place."

He said: "What made you do that?"

He said: "We monkeys have the habit, when we go out visiting our friends, of leaving our hearts behind in order to avert suspicion from us. If you want me to bring you it, though, I'll do so."

The tortoise was happy at the monkey's kindness about his heart, and he hurried back with him. When he reached the shore, the monkey leaped to the ground, ran to the tree, and climbed it.

The tortoise waited an hour for him, As he was making him wait so long, he called out to him:

"Hurry up, my friend! Pick up your heart and come down, for you're holding me up."

The monkey said: "I see you're thinking I'm like the donkey whom the jackal said had no heart or ears."

The tortoise said: "How was that?"

The monkey said:

[A. The Donkey without Ears or Heart]

"Once upon a time a lion lived in a lair with a jackal who ate whatever was left over of his game. A violent rash attacked the lion so that he became weak and worn out. He could not hunt, so the jackal said to the lion:

" 'What is wrong with you, O lord of beasts? Indeed your lot has changed!'

"He said: 'All on account of this rash which you see. There is no remedy for it unless I secure a donkey's ears and heart.'

"The jackal said: 'I know where there is a donkey who goes to a meadow near us with a laundryman who loads him with the clothes he washes. When he unloads his clothes, he turns him loose in the meadow. I expect I can bring him to you. Then you can take his heart and ears.'

"The lion said: 'Get busy on that right away!'

"So the jackal went off to the donkey and said to him: 'Why are you so lean and have welts on your back?'

"The donkey said: 'I belong to this wretched laundryman, and he spoils my fodder and goads me to work.'

"The jackal said: 'How do you put up with that?'

"He said: 'What else can I do? How can I escape from men's hands?'

"The jackal said: 'I'll show you an out-of-the-way pasture where man never goes at all. Yonder there are jennies the like of which you have never seen, beautiful and well-bred; and they need some males.'

"The donkey became excited and said: 'Why don't you take us along? I want nothing better than your friendship! That is why I'm going away with you.'

"So they both went off together to meet the lion. The jackal went ahead and informed him. The lion sprang upon the donkey, but he did not pin him down, and so the donkey slipped away.

"The jackal said to the lion: 'What is this you have done? If you let go of the donkey on purpose, why did you bother me with hunting him up? If you are such that you can't catch him, it is our ruin if our lord cannot pin down a donkey.'

"The lion knew that if he said: 'I let him go on purpose', he would lose face with him; while if he said: 'I could not catch him', he would seem weak. So he said:

" 'If you are able to bring the donkey back, then I'll tell you what you asked me about him.'

"The jackal said: 'The donkey has experienced plenty from me, but I'll still try to do what I can with him once more.'

"So he went back to the donkey. When the latter saw him, he said: 'What 'treachery$^{9)}$ did you want with me?'

"He said: 'I only wanted to do you good, but the fault was in your being too eager. What leaped upon you was one of the jennies I told you about. I had already told you that you had never seen their like, and she jumped on you, she was so eager. If you had only waited an hour for her, she would have got under you. The blame is only in that she is so in heat.'

"When the donkey heard the jennies mentioned for the second time, his lust was kindled and he went away with him. The lion leaped upon him and slew him.

"When the lion had finished killing the donkey, he said to the jackal: 'This is the medicine prescribed for me, so I shall wash myself, then eat the ears and heart and make the proper sacrifice. So guard the donkey while I wash myself; then I'll return.'

"When the lion went away, the jackal went straight to the donkey's ears and heart. He ate them up in the hope that the lion would notice it and not eat the remainder of the donkey nor sacrifice from it.[5]

"When the lion returned, he said: 'Where are the donkey's heart and ears?'

"The jackal said: "Didn't you notice that the donkey had neither heart nor ears? If he had had them, he would never have returned to you once he had managed to escape.'

"And the lion believed him.

"I have made up this story for you to let you know that I am not like the donkey whom the jackal said had no heart or ears. You thought you could fool and cheat me. I paid you back in the same coin as you paid me, and averted what I was slipping into by myself."

The tortoise said: "You are a trustworthy and truthful person, and I know that any intelligent man spares his words, fulfills his obligations, and acknowledges any fault. He understands matters before coming up against them, and makes up for any mistake he has committed by his own actions, like the man who stumbles upon the ground, and in getting up leans upon the same ground."

This fable is about a man who seeks something
until he loses it just when he has it
within his grasp.

Here Ends the Chapter of the Monkey and the Tortoise.

Chapter VI

Of the Hermit and the Mongoose[1]

[Or the Fruit of Hasty Action]

HE KING said to the philosopher: "I have heard this fable, so if you see fit, compose me one about a man who is hasty in matters and acts without investigation or consideration."

Bidpai the philosopher said: "Whoever is not of an investigating turn of mind in his business and deeds, always regrets it. One of those stories is the fable of the hermit and the mongoose."

The king said: "What was that?"

The philosopher said:

ONCE UPON A TIME a hermit lived in the country of Jarkan. He had a wife who remained for a long time without having any children. Then she became pregnant, and the hermit said to her in his glee:

"Rejoice, for I expect you will bear a boy who will be a pleasure to us and a delight to our eyes! I am going out to look for a nurse for him, and the best name I can find."

The woman said: "Husband, what teaches you to talk like this when you don't know (whether[Sp]) I shall have a child or how the offspring will turn out? Keep quiet about this and be pleased with whatever God may bestow upon you! The intelligent man does not talk when he doesn't know how things will turn out, nor makes wild guesses; but he arrives at his decision through prayer, being neither desperate nor over-confident.

"Whoever speaks about something he does not know about, and feels capable of handling some matter, will have happen to him what happened to the hermit who poured butter and honey on his head."

The hermit said: "How was that?"

The woman said:

[A. The Monk and the Jar of Butter and Honey]²

"Once upon a time a hermit used to receive a steady allowance of butter, honey, and porridge from a certain merchant's house. He used to save some of that butter and honey, place it in a jug he had, ʿand hang it on a peg in the wall of his houseⁿ. He did so until he filled the jug.

"Now it happened that the price of butter and honey went up. ʿOne day while the hermit was lying on his back with a staff in his hand and the jar hanging above his head, he thought about the high price of butter and honeyⁿ.

"So he said: 'I am going to sell what is in this jar for at least one dinar. With that dinar I shall buy ten goats, and they will conceive and bear in five months.'

"He conjectured in this way for a period of five years, and according to his calculations found he would come out with more than four hundred goats.

"Then he said: 'Thus I'll buy a hundred cows, trading four goats for every bull or cow. I shall then obtain seedgrain and sow with the bulls; while I'll profit from the bellies of the females and their milk. Will not five years bring me much wealth from my increase and the seed? Thus I shall have a splendid house built, and buy salves and garments and furniture.

" 'When I have finished with that, I shall marry a beautiful woman of good family, and when I have consummated the marriage, I shall cause her to conceive. Then she will bear me a fine son, handsome, blessed, and honest, and I shall name him appropriately. I shall give him an excellent education and shall be strict in punishing him: if I see him acting foolishly and he does not heed me, I shall beat his head with this stick like this!'

"He raised the stick to show off with it, and hit the jug. It broke, and the butter and honey poured all over his head, and his projects and wishes turned out to be in vain.

"I have only made this story up so you can stop talking about what you don't know whether fate is to bring you."

The hermit heeded what she said. Then the woman bore a perfect boy, and his father was happy.

Some days later, the wife said to her husband: "Sit down with the lad until I wash myself and return."

The woman went away, and the man had scarcely sat down when a messenger arrived from the sultan ʿand asked him to go along for some ceremony$^{Sp)}$. He went off with him, leaving no one with his son except a tame mongoose which guarded the boy like a person would. The man left him in charge, and went off to the sultan.

In his house there was a snake's hole, and the snake came out to get the boy. The mongoose sprang upon it and tore it to pieces, ʿand scattered blood all over$^{Y/CɛD)}$.

The hermit returned from his mission, and as he was coming into the house, the mongoose met him, running to greet him with what he had done. When the hermit saw him smeared with blood, he lost his mind, ʿthinking it had killed his son$^{Y/CɛD)}$. He did not wait to investigate, but dealt the mongoose a blow on the head with his stick, and it fell down dead.

The hermit entered his house, and saw the boy ʿalive and safe$^{Sp)}$ and the snake ripped up. He understood matters, and started to say:

"Would that this boy had never been born, and I had not committed this treachery and sin!"

The woman came in whilst he was lamenting so, and she said to him: "Why are you crying? What's the matter with this snake and mongoose, which have been killed?"

He told her what had happened to both of them, saying: "This is the fruit of hasty action!"

This is the fable about him who acts without thinking about what he is doing.

Here Ends the Chapter of the Hermit and the Mongoose[3]

Chapter VII

The Chapter of
Ayladh, Shadaram, and Irakhat
[Or Don't Trust Priests][1]

ING DABSHALIM said to Bidpai the philosopher: "I have understood what you have told me about taking hasty action without being sure of oneself or making previous investigation. Now tell me how a king acts generously towards his subjects, consolidates his rule, and defends his land: is it through forebearance, manliness in self-defence, ⟨courage$^{Y/CɛD}$⟩, or generosity?"

The philosopher said: "The most distinguished way of attaining that is by forebearance or intelligence, since they are the chief things and they support the rest; plus the advice of a keen-witted, reliable sage. Yet the most useful thing which people, and especially a king, can enjoy is forebearance, for there is nothing more distinguished or helpful than it.

"A man's salvation lies in living with an honest, far-sighted, compliant wife; for even if a man is a courageous leader and does not have some forebearant and wise individual to advise him, and thus he consults with someone who is not keen-witted, then a simple matter will bother him until he sees how ugly and weak is his ignorance, and his companion's error in judgment. Even if he chances upon success or is led towards a good end by fate and keeps on steadily towards it, he comes to regret the consequences of his deed.

"When it is otherwise, through his minister's superior influence, then fortune favors him and he achieves success against whoever is opposing him, victory over whoever was resisting him, and happiness from whatever was afflicting him. We have been told this is what passed between Shadaram, the king of India, Irakhat his consort, and Ayladh his privy counsellor."

The king said: "How was that?"

The philosopher said:

[A. The King and the Priests]

ONCE UPON A TIME there lived Ayladh, a zealous ascetic of fine character, gentle, forebearant, and a perfect sage. Meanwhile Shadaram, the king, was sleeping in his chamber one night, when he saw eight dreams. At each of the dreams, he woke up.

'Now the vision was as follows: two red trout came towards him balancing on their tails, with two ducks flying from behind and stopping in front of them, and a snake which jumped at his feet. He also saw that his body was bathed in blood, and that his body had been washed with water. He noticed he was standing on a white mountain, and saw that something like fire covered his head, and a white bird was pecking his head with her beak[Sp)].

When it dawned, he called Brahmans, who are monks,[2] and told them what he had seen, and ordered them to interpret it.

They said: "You have seen, O king, a strange and loathsome thing which has not been heard of in times past. If you want, we shall go off and ponder over it for six days. On the sixth day we shall come back and inform you about it; and if perchance we have been enabled to defend you from what you are fearing, we shall do so."

The king said: "Yes, act according to what you think will suit me."

They said: "Of course."

So they left his presence, and gathered together and said: "It is not such a long time since he killed twelve thousand of us.[3] We gained control of him when he revealed his secret to us and informed us how frightened he is of his vision. Perhaps we shall take revenge on him if we speak harshly and inspire fear in him so that he will obey us in whatever we may want. Let's order him to hand us over those of his family and ministers whom he honors.

"We shall say to him: 'We have looked into our books and do not find anything to avert what you tell us, except killing those we mention to you.'

"And if he says: 'Whom do you mean?' we shall say:

" 'Your wife Irakhat, Jawir your son, and your sister's son. And Ayladh your secretary (for he is cunning and wise); and Kal, your scribe and spokesman. And your sword, and the white elephant on which you fight. And the two great elephants and the steed upon which you ride, and the Bactrian camel on which you travel. And Kanan Abzun, the jurist.

" 'Put their blood in a copper basin in which we shall seat you, and when we decide to take you out of it, we Brahmans will gather together as a body from four sides. We shall bewitch you and charm you and wash you with water and goodly ointments. Then we shall take you to your council-hall, and God will remove the dreadful part of what you have seen.

" 'If you endure this and delight in it yourself, you shall be freed from your torment and escape from the calamity which is opressing and overwhelming you. You will soon have others in place of them; while if you do not do so, we dread lest you may be carried off forcibly and done away with. Your kingdom will be seized, and your offspring uprooted.' "

When the Brahmans had polished up their argument and agreed upon it, they came to the king and said: "We have looked into our books and have studied them, and pondered over your vision and racked our brains. It is not in our power to tell you what we think until you speak with us in private."

He did so, and they told him the matter which they had already arranged.

The king said: "Death is better than what I have heard! How am I to begin killing these persons who are like my own self, and bear such a burden and crime? There is no escape from death in any case, and I will not be in this kingdom of mine for eternity. It is the same to me whether I perish or am separated from my loved ones!"

The Brahmans said: "If you will not become angry, we shall show you how your opinion is mistaken. Indeed, you are not acting rightly when you despise yourself and honor others more. Don't you know that everything else is trifling, and nothing is of any benefit, no matter how lofty its size or how small?

"Upon my life, the best solution is to redeem it with those we have named to you, for you will remain in your kingdom and sovereignty and save your administration. Look to it, and give up whatever else there is, for nothing is equal to it!"

When the king saw that the Brahmans were using harsh language and acting boldly towards him, he stood up and went inside. He fell upon his face and began to writhe, worried and saddened; and he thought over which course to take: allowing the death of important people, or not giving in to what they asked.

He dwelt upon that for some days, and the news spread thoughout his land. It was murmured:

"Something has happened to the king which is grieving him!"

When Ayladh saw what had befallen the king, he reflected and meditated, for he was open-minded and knowing, experienced and shrewd. So he said:

"I should not bring up anything with the king before he calls on me; but I shall go to Irakhat, the king's consort, and ask her about this."

So he went to her and said: "I don't know of the king embarking upon any affair large or small since I am with him, except with my advice. I was his secretary, and he concealed nothing that happened to him. Whenever any critical situation afflicted him, he consoled himself and bore whatever befell him patiently, mentioning it to me so I might dispel it as gently as I could.

"Now I see he had an audience with the Brahmans a week ago, and has kept apart from people since that time. I am afraid that he has told them some of his most private affairs, and I don't trust them. So you go and ask him about his condition and what they say has happened to him; then let me know, for I am not able to get in to see him. I reckon they have prettied up some hideous thing and loaded him with slander, making him angry about something spurious.

"In fact, one of the king's habits when enraged, is not to consult or ask about anything, nor even to consider important or paltry matters. Doubtless they did not advise him honestly because of their rancor and hatred for him; for if they can catch and ruin him, they will seek to have this happen to him."

Irakhat said: "The king and I had words, and I do not care to go to him so long as he feels offended."

Ayladh said: "Don't let a grudge keep you away on such a day as this, for no one can go into him besides you. I have heard him say on different occasions: 'When I am sad and worried, and Irakhat comes to me, all that leaves me!' So go and tell him what you think will do his soul good, and give him some consolation."

When Irakhat heard that, she rose up and went to see the king. She went in to him, and sat down at his head and said:

"What is the matter, O happy, upright, and praiseworthy king? What did the Brahmans say to you; for I see you are worried and sad? If you must contrive something to dispel your worry and ⟨un^{Sp)}⟩happiness, and it will help to end our lives, then do so. If you harbor any anger towards us, we will satisfy you and offer whatever will gladden you.

⟨"I see you are so sad and depressed and worried that it weighs upon my heart. I can't be sad about something I don't know, for a king is to his people as the head is to the body; when the head is well, the body is well. And we cannot be gay while our king is sad and depressed^{Sp)}!"

The king said: "My wife, don't ask me about anything: you will only increase the turmoil which afflicts me! You oughtn't to know that matter so fraught with danger and mighty in terror."

Irakhat said: "My dealings with you have come to the pass where you answer me as I have heard! Don't you know that the best idea for a king when he is overwhelmed, is to seek advice from his sincere friends and loved ones, who will assume his worries and grief for him? For a culprit does not despair of mercy, but repents for what he fears.

"Don't let the worry and grief which I see take possession of you, for neither will avert anything but rather gladden one's enemies and grieve one's friends. Clever and experienced people realize that and conceal their disappointments, and they settle down with whatever events may bring."

The king said: "O wife, don't ask me anything, for what you are trying to find out concerns my ruin and the destruction of your boy and many of the people I love. The Brahmans say there is no way out but killing you and them; and there is no good in my living after you, nor any pleasure in being separated from you. That makes matters difficult and worries me greatly."

⟨When^{Sp)}⟩ Irakhat ⟨heard^{Sp)}⟩ this, ⟨she showed no fright, but smilingly^{Sp)}⟩ said: "God is not saddening nor has grieved you, O king; our souls are a ransom and a pledge for you. Indeed that is trifling provided you can remain safe. God has already granted you other wives as a substitute and a consolation.

"But I beseech you that after my death you will not trust the

Brahmans nor ask their advice nor kill anyone until you have consulted people who will advise you sincerely, and whom you trust
and know how to proceed with. For killing is a serious business
and a grievous sin, and you are never able to bring back to life
what you have done away with.

"It has been said: If you find a jewel you don't think is any
good, and want to 'throw$^{Y/CeD)}$ it away, don't do so until you show
it to someone who will assay it. Don't hearten your enemies
among the Brahmans and others; know that they have never
advised you sincerely, and only recently you killed twelve thousand of them. Do you think they have forgotten that?

"Upon my life, you ought not to have told them about your
vision nor let them in on your secret! For from what they have
mentioned about your vision, they only want to ruin you, to destroy your loved ones, and to do away with your ministers, who are
men of prudence, knowledge, and wisdom, and the means by
which you may defeat them.

"But go look for Kanan Abzun and tell him your case, and ask
him about what appeared to you. He is keen-witted and trustworthy, and there is no one superior to him in anything. It is as
though he were born a Brahman, although he is only a hermit
versed in the law. If he gives you the same advice as their sentence, then heed it; while if his judgment disagrees with what they
say, keep still and don't do anything about the matter."

When the king heard her say that, he was astonished, and
ordered his steed saddled. Then he rode off in haste towards
Kanan Abzun's.

When he came up to him, he alighted from his steed. Then he
bowed down and greeted him, inclining his head in reverence.

Kanan Abzun said to him: "Whatever has happened to you, O
king? Why do I see you altered in color and filled with sorrow?
Nor do I see your turban on you, nor your king's crown."

The king said to him: "One night I was sleeping in the rear of
my palace, when I heard eight sounds underground. I awakened at
each sound, and then went back to sleep. I saw eight visions, and
described them to the Brahmans, for I was afraid that a serious
thing would happen to me; either that I would be killed in battle,
or that my kingdom would be snatched away and myself defeated."

Kanan Abzun said: "Don't let this matter sadden nor frighten you! You won't die nor be deprived of your kingdom, nor will any of the crimes and evils which you dread happen to you. As for the eight dreams which you saw, recount them and I will reveal their interpretation to you."

The king described the visions, and Kanan Abzun said to him:

"As for the two red fish which stood up on their tails, they are coming to you as messenger from King Hamyun of 'Niazor^{Sp)}4 with two 'necklaces covered with pearls and rubies worth four thousand gold pounds, which they will present to you^{η)}. The two ducks which you saw flying from behind you and alighting in front of you are coming from the king of Bactria, who will appear with two steeds whose like is not to be found on earth. The snake which you saw crawling at your left foot is coming from King Sakhin 'of India^{Sp)} with a sword of pure iron whose mate is not to be found.

"What you saw as you were staining your body with blood, is coming to you from King Kasrun, who is appearing before you with marvellous garments called purple brocade, which shines in the dark. As for when you saw yourself washing your body in water, it meant that 'linen^{Y/CeD)} clothes like kings wear are coming to you from the King of Raz.

"When you saw yourself upon a white mountain, that meant that King Khayar is sending you a 'white elephant.^{Y/CeD} And what seemed like fire on your head^{Sp)} is a gold tiara 'which a king^{Sp} of Arzan^Y will be sending you^{Sp)}. The white bird which beat your head with its beak is something I am not going to explain to you today; but it will not hurt you and do not 'fear^{Y/CeD)} it. However, it contains something to make you angry and annoyed with those you love.

"These couriers and messengers will all appear before you within seven days."

When the king heard that, he bowed down before Kanan Abzun. Then he went away saying: "I will look into what he said."

When it was the seventh day, the king dressed up in his garments and took out his ornaments. He sat down on his throne and gave audience to his grandees and nobles. Those gifts which Kanan Abzun had prophesied to him arrived, and they were placed before him.

When the king saw those couriers and messengers, along with those gifts, his joy increased and he said to himself:

"I did not act properly that time I told the Brahmans my dream and they ordered me to do that. If it were not that God had protected and shown mercy to me, and favored me with Irakhat's advice, I should have perished and passed out of this world.

"Therefore everyone ought to listen to the opinion of his intimates and loved ones and kinsfolk, and accept their advice. Irakhat gave me her opinion, and I accepted it and am happy. My kingdom has been strengthened by my intimates' and sound advisers' opinion, and it is clear to me how wise is Kanan Abzun and how honest in what he says."

Then the king called Jawir, Ayladh, and Kal the scribe, and said to them: "We should not put these gifts in our treasury, but I shall divide them amongst you who chose death for my sake, and with Irakhat who gave me the advice which was instrumental in saving my kingdom and for which you now see me so full of joy and happiness."

Ayladh said: "A group of servants like us should not be amazed at what we had to do, for a servant ought to deliver himself up to death in place of his master. As for these presents, we servants ought not to approach them. Jawir, your son, is worthy of them; so let him take whatever you give him."

The king said: "Indeed we are overwhelmed by this fine praise and great kindness! Do not get excited, Ayladh; take your share. Let your eye be delighted with it."

Ayladh said: "May that be as the king wishes. Let's begin by taking what we want."

So the king took the white elephant, and gave Jawir one of the two steeds. He gave Ayladh the pure iron sword, and Kal the scribe the other horse, and sent Kanan Abzun the robes such as kings wear. As for the tiara and other garments which were suitable only for women, he said to Ayladh:

"Take the tiara and garments, and carry them along to the women for me."

So the king called Irakhat and Kuraqanah [his second wife]. They both sat down before him, and the king said:

"Ayladh, place the tiara and the suit of clothes before Irakhat, and let her take whichever she prefers."

When Irakhat saw the tiara and admired it, she looked at Ayladh out of the corner of her eye to see which were preferable. Ayladh pointed out the clothes to her, and advised her to take them.

Just then the king turned and saw Ayladh. When Irakhat noticed that the king had seen him wink at her, she dropped what Ayladh had pointed out and took the tiara.

Ayladh lived for forty years after that, and whenever he entered the king's presence, he blinked his eyes so that the king would not think he had seen anything. If both Irakhat and Ayladh had not been clever, neither one of them would have escaped death!

[B. The King and the Queen]

Now the king used to spend one night with Irakhat and one night with Kuraqanah; and so he came to Irakhat on her night, and she prepared some rice for him.[5] She came in to the king with a gold dish in her hand and the tiara upon her head. She stood before the king with the dish, and he ate from it.

When Kuraqanah saw the crown on Irakhat's head, she became jealous of Irakhat, put on those clothes, and remained dazzling like the sun. She passed before the king, and he beheld Kuraqanah and said to Irakhat:

"You were silly the time you took the tiara and left the clothes whose like was not in my treasurehouse!"

When Irakhat heard how he spoke to her and praised Kuraqanah, and how silly he considered her judgment, she was filled with rage and anger, and beat the king over the head with the dish in her hand so that the rice poured over his head and body. That was the interpretation of the dream which Kanan Abzun did not 'disclose*Y/CєD*' to the king nor explain to him.

So the king summoned Ayladh and said: "Ayladh, don't you see how this woman has mocked the king of the world and done this to him? Take her away and chop off her head and have no mercy on her!"

Ayladh left the king's presence with Irakhat, saying to himself: "I am not for killing her until the king's anger subsides, for she is an intelligent woman, the happiest of queens. She has no equal among women in forebearance and intelligence, and the king will not last long without her. Up till today she has saved many men from death, and has performed many good deeds. We still expect great things from her; and I am not confident that he will not say: 'Weren't you able to postpone killing her?'

"I am not going to kill her until I see what the king's opinion about her will be. If he repents and is sad about killing her, I shall bring her back alive. I shall have done three important deeds: I shall save Irakhat from being killed, and console the king's grief; 'then the king will appreciate me ahead of all the men in the world; and thirdly, the king will know he shouldn't act hastily⁵⁾. If he does not mention her, I shall fulfill his order concerning her."⁶

So Ayladh went off home secretly and entrusted her to two trustworthy king's men who watched his women. He ordered his people to guard and honor her until he saw the outcome of the affair.

Then Ayladh stained his sword with blood and went in sorrowful and sad, and said to the king: "I carried out your order concerning Irakhat."

It was not long before the king's anger subsided, and he remembered Irakhat's beauty, judgment, sympathy, and great usefulness. His sadness increased, and his heart began to struggle and wrestle. He was ashamed to ask Ayladh whether he had really carried out his order or not, but he began to hope that he had not killed her, since he knew how intelligent Ayladh was.

Ayladh perceived this with his splendid insight, and he said: "May God neither sadden nor worry the king, for there is no advantage in worrying or being sad. It wears you out physically and spoils things, besides making the king's people also sad when he is melancholy, and his enemies joyful and happy. If he were overheard, he would not be considered intelligent or wise. So be patient, your majesty, and not sad about what you can never see. If the king wants, I shall tell him a story similar to his own."

The king said: "Tell me it."

Ayladh said:

[B.1 The Two Pigeons]

"Once upon a time two pigeons, male and female, filled their nest with wheat and barley. The cock said to the hen:

" 'As long as we find what we can live off in the wilderness, let's not eat anything which is in our nest. When winter comes and we do not discover anything in the wilderness, we may have recourse to what we have gathered and eat it.'

"The hen consented to that and said: 'What you think is fine; we shall do as you say.'

"Now the wheat and barley had been damp at the time they were placed there. They filled their nest, and the male went off somewhere. He was absent quite a while because something held him up. When it came summer, that grain dried up and withered, and shrank from what it had been.

"When the cock returned and saw the grain was less, he said: 'We agreed not to eat anything from our nest! Why did you eat some?'

"The female swore: 'I didn't eat a grain of it; 'but it diminished with the bad weather, which is hot and dry*Sp).*'

"But he did not believe her and started to peck her to death.

"When winter came on with the rains, the grain became damp and filled the nest as before. When the male saw that the nest was full again, he lay down beside it disconsolate and said:

" 'How can I go on living when I look for you and cannot find you?'

"Whoever is intelligent knows that he should not be hasty in chastising or punishing anyone, especially if it means inflicting a punishment he may come to regret just as the male pigeon did. 'And you, sire, should not seek what you cannot find; so forget this trouble and cleave to what you still have. Do not be like the monkey with the lentils!"

The King said: "How was that*Sp)*?

[Ayladh said:]

[B.2 The Monkey and the Lentils]

"I have heard that a man had a bundle of lentils on his back. He went in among some trees and put down his load. Then he fell asleep, 'because he was tired*Sp)*.

"A monkey came down from a tree overhead, and took a handful of those lentils. Then as he was climbing back up the tree, a grain fell out of his hand. He 'climbed down to*Sp)* look for it, and did not find it.

"'In swinging down from limb to limb⁽ˢᵖ⁾', he scattered the rest of the grain in his hand. 'He did not get the first, and he lost all the rest he had⁽ˢᵖ⁾.

"You, O king, have sixteen thousand women, and let yourself be diverted from them to seek what you do not find!"

When the king heard that, he fancied that Irakhat had perished. He said to Ayladh:

"With one slip, I made you do what I ordered at your own time. You hung upon just one word! Did you not confirm the order?"

Ayladh said: "He whose word is uniform is not altered by me."

The king said: "Who is that?"

Ayladh said: "That is God, who neither changes His word, nor fails to follow up what He says."

The king said: "Indeed my sadness has increased with the killing of Irakhat, the mother of Jawir."

Ayladh said: "'Two ought to be quite saddened: he who sins ᵞ/ᶜᵉᴰ every day,ᵞ and he who never does any good; for both have little joy in this world, and then they go to lasting sadness ᵞ/ᶜᵉᴰ.'"

The king said: "If I should see Irakhat alive, I would never be sad about anything!"

Ayladh said: "Two are those who ought not to be sad: he who strives after good works every day; and he who does not sit at all."

The king said: "I shall never see Irakhat, excepting what I have already seen 'of her⁽ˢᵖ⁾."

Ayladh said: "Two never see: the blind man; and he who has no brains. For just as the blind man does not notice the sky nor the stars nor the earth, and does not distinguish what is far from what is near, nor what is before him nor behind him; even so he who has no intelligence, neither notices nor tells the difference between the wise man and the ignorant, the beautiful and the ugly, nor the well-doer and the evil-doer."

The king said: "If I saw Irakhat, my joy would increase."

Ayladh said: "Two are those who see: the observant man; and the wise man. For just as the observant man notices the light of the world and what is in it, so does the wise man observe good works and sin, and knows the things of the other world which are clear to him. When he follows them, they save him and guide him to the straight path."

The king said: "I was never sated of seeing Irakhat!"

Ayladh said to him: "Two are those who are never sated: he who has no other concern than collecting wealth; and he who eats what there is, and then asks for what doesn't exist."

The king said: "We ought to shun you, Ayladh, for one has to be wary and keep away from your type."

Ayladh said: "Two should be shunned: he who says there are no good works and no sin; and he who is unable to keep his eyes off what is not his, nor his ears from listening to evil, nor his private parts from other people's women, nor his heart from what torments his soul with sin and hankering. Thereby he chooses repentance and the dread of hell's torment."

The king said: "I have become empty (without Irakhat$^{Y/CeD)}$."

Ayladh said: "(Four$^{\eta}$ things are empty: the river which has no water; the land without a king; the woman with no husband; and another is he who does not return good for evil nor perform any good works."

The king said: "You always find the answer, Ayladh!"

Ayladh said: "Three are those who find the answer: the king who divides up and gives away his treasure; the woman ready for any person of quality she may desire; and the wise man divinely aided who teaches God's law."

The king said: "Really you sadden me with your condolence, Ayladh."

Ayladh said: "Three are those who should be sad: he whose steed is fat and handsome, but still badly trained; the owner of a stew with lots of water and little meat, so that it turns out to have little food value; and he who marries a beautiful woman of fine lineage and then cannot keep up her self-respect, so that she is always making him listen to what pains him."

The king said: "Irakhat perished in vain (and^{Sp} without reason$^{Y/CeD)}$."

Ayladh said: 'Three things are lost without reason: the (blacksmith$^{\eta}$ who dresses up in white clothes and keeps on sitting by his bellows; the fuller who puts on new yellow boots and stands with his feet in the water; and the merchant who marries a beautiful young woman and is always travelling abroad."

The king said: "You are one of those people who should be punished severely, Ayladh."

Ayladh said: "Three ought to be punished:7 the criminal (judge$^{Sp)}$

who punishes the not guilty; the forward individual sitting at a table where he is not invited; and he who asks his friends for what they do not have, and keeps right on asking them for it."

The king said: "You ought to be considered foolish, Ayladh."[8]

Ayladh said: "Three ought to be considered foolish. The carpenter who lives in a small house with his family, and then keeps on cutting up wood and filling his house with kindling so that he and his wife live in cramped quarters. The surgeon who works with the scalpel without taking precautions, so that he cuts men's flesh needlessly. And the foreigner who stays with his enemy's people and does not care to return to his own people and place of origin, so that if he dies while he is still abroad, they are his heirs and his wealth belongs to strangers and his memory is wiped out."

The king said: "You ought to have waited until my anger subsided."

Ayladh said: "Three ought to wait: he who climbs a tall mountain; he who goes fishing; and he who is worried about doing something important."

The king said: "Would that I might see Irakhat!"

Ayladh said: "Three long for what they do not find; the libertine who has no godliness and wants to be considered a well-doer when he dies and expects to earn the same reward; the miser who wants the rank of a noble for himself; and criminals who shed blood without reason, and hope their souls will be with the souls of the God-fearing and blissful, the people of compassion and mercy."

The king said: "My heart aches for Irakhat!"[9]

Ayladh said: "Three are those whose heart aches. He who goes forth to battle and does not watch out so that he gets killed. The wealthy individual who has neither a son nor a brother, when his trade consists of usury and profiteering, even though many people may envy him. And the fine old man who marries a beautiful though immoral woman who goes boldly after her whims and keeps wanting his death so that she may marry a different and younger husband, and thus holds the key to his destruction."

The king said: "I am indeed despicable in your eyes, Ayladh, when you dare to talk to me like this!"

Ayladh said: "Three despise their masters: he who havers in his speech and interferes whether he is asked or not, and talks about anything whether he knows it or not; the bondsman[10] who is rich while his master is poor, and does not give his master any of his wealth nor assist him with it; and the slave who talks rudely to his master and quarrels with him and then finally defeats him in a lawsuit."

The king said: "How you abash me, Ayladh! I wish that Irakhat were not dead."

Ayladh said: "Three ought to be abashed. He who says: 'I have enlisted in many armies, done much fighting, and taken many prisoners', while no mark of battle is to be found on his body. Then he who gives out that he is learned in religion and a zealous ascetic, while his neck bulges out and is fatter than a sinner's or libertine's; so he ought to be scoffed at and suspected for what he says about himself, since whoever devotes himself to God's service becomes lean in body and a small eater. And [finally] the woman who makes fun of getting married, while she is probably quite loose herself."[11]

The king said: "You are presumptuous, Ayladh."

Ayladh said: "Three appear as presumptuous as if they rave along with the devils. The ignorant man who teaches a fool to argue with him in his ignorance; he accomplishes nothing except having to regret his action. He who provokes a simpleton and picks a fight with him, intending to annoy and confuse him, while he only injures himself. And he who tells a secret to someone with whom he should not be on speaking terms, letting him know some important matter and confiding in him as if in himself."

The king said: "I am worrying myself."

Ayladh said: "Two are those who worry themselves. He who runs away from retribution by turning his back on it, often stumbling and rolling into a well or falling into a ravine and smashing himself. And he who says: 'I never flinch in battle or dread it', in order to fool others; while when people are present, he turns right and left seeking a chance to escape."

The king said: "Whatever was between you and me has ended, Ayladh!"

Ayladh said: "Three quickly end their affection: the friend who does not come halfway nor correspond with his friend nor even enquires after him; the friend whose loved ones honor him, and he does not take it at its face value nor welcome them warmly, but makes fun of and sneers at them; and he who seeks his friends when they furnish him pleasure and joy and consolation, and when he asks them for something they cannot provide him, never returns to them for anything."

The king said: "By killing Irakhat, you did something which shows your fickleness of purpose, Ayladh."

Ayladh said: "Three work with fickleness of purpose, judging by the results which are shown: the man who deposits his wealth with someone whose sense of justice towards a litigant he does not know; and the cowardly, small-witted simpleton who tells people he is brave in battle, clear-sighted in earning wealth, choosing friends, constructing buildings, and resolving upon an important deed, while he is lying about everything he mentions; and he who publishes that he is abandoning material matters to deal with affairs of the spirit, while he only intends to follow his own passions and abandon God's commands and the fulfillment of His will."

The king said: "You are not intelligent, Ayladh."

Ayladh said: "Three ought not to be counted as men of intelligence: the cobbler who sits upon a platform so that when his knife or some other tool rolls off, it distracts him from much of his work; the tailor whose thread is so long that when he ties a knot in it, it distracts him from his work; and he who turns right and left while cutting people's hair and snarls it, so that he deserves to be punished for his clumsiness."[12]

The king said: "It seems that you want to instruct everybody till they become as skilled as you, and you want to teach me also so I may be skilled."

Ayladh said: "Three [trades], they relate, are skilled and ought to be taught: he who plays the cymbals, lute, and kettledrum to accompany the flute and other melodies; the painter who draws a good line in paintings but does not mix his colors well; and he who asserts that he does not require knowledge about any trade, for he knows every trade and craft, but does not understand the meaning of a word nor how it goes, nor at what time he ought to speak with whoever is above or beneath him."

The king said: "You didn't act rightly when you killed Irakhat."

Ayladh said: "Four act other than rightly: he whose tongue is not truthful and who does not watch what he says; one hasty in eating and slow in working, fighting, and serving his superiors; he who is unable to calm his anger before he commits a crime; and the king who plans a great affair and then abandons it."

The king said: "If you had acted according to my custom, you would not have killed Irakhat."

Ayladh said: "Four act according to custom: he who prepares food at the right time, and arranges and brings it to his master just when he wants it; he who desires only one woman and keeps his private parts from other women who are not permitted him; the king who accomplishes a great deed upon the advice of wise men; and the man who restrains his anger."

The king said: "I am really afraid of you, Ayladh."

Ayladh said: "Four are afraid of what they ought not fear: the little bird who sits on a tree and holds one of his feet up in fear lest the sky should fall upon him, saying: 'If the sky falls, I'll hold it up with my foot!'; the crane who is standing on just one leg in fear lest the earth will cave in on him if he puts the other one down; the worm in the earth eating dirt, who does not eat enough to satisfy itself in fear lest the dirt in the earth should disappear through his eating it, and he is therefore worried and sad in fear lest it will die of hunger; and the bat who refrains from flying by day, thinking that there is no bird on earth more handsome than it, and fears lest men will hunt it to lock it up with them."[13]

The king said: "Did you swear to kill Irakhat?"

Ayladh said: "Four ought to be sworn never to be banished: the fleet and valuable horse who is his master's pride; the bull with which you plow; the intelligent woman who is beloved of her husband; and the energetic slave, sincere in service, and honest and attentive towards his master."

The king said: "I don't see anybody else like Irakhat!"

Ayladh said: "Four cannot be found alike: the woman who has tried out several husbands and just wants one man; the man who has accustomed his tongue to lying and then starts to tell the truth; the man who so admires his own judgment that he becomes an easy mark or makes friends with his enemy; and the vain man who is against everything around him, if he changes his disposition so that he becomes peaceful."

The king said: "Would that this knowledge had been shown before today! Today it gives me little contentment or profit."

Ayladh said: "The knowledge of three things ought to be known beforehand; of a warlike man with power over his enemies, before one may need anything of that sort from him; concerning whoever litigates about a valuable thing with a man who esteems his own judgment but has no intelligence, so that he needs to take steps to secure an impartial, disinterested, and wise judge who will not decide by whim nor accept bribes to reach a decision in any case; and after a man makes an appointment with an illustrious man to dine, he should start preparing food and whatever else goes with it, so that he will not be in a rush to prepare and procure it, and he and his family thus land in turmoil."

The king said: "Neither innocence do you know, nor guilt, Ayladh."

Ayladh said: "Four do not think about innocence or guilt: the sick man with a serious illness; he who fears his master; he who is watching for a chance to pay back his enemy; and the brave yet despised man who has been wronged and is not overawed by someone stronger than himself."

The king said: "Indeed you have lost virtue, Ayladh."

Ayladh said: "Four are they who have lost virtue: he who fills his body with wickedness and crime; the outcast who admires himself; he who has become accustomed to stealing; and the man quick to wrath and slow to be satisfied."

The king said: "We should not trust you, Ayladh."

Ayladh said: "Four are not to be trusted: the roused snake; every beast that is feared by living creatures; confirmed criminals; and the envious[14] man, for he is as good as condemned to death."

The king said: "Dignified persons should not laugh or joke."

Ayladh said: "Four ought not to laugh or joke: the king who is a real monarch; the devout ascetic; the man who is shrewd though humble; and the villainous character who is of a greedy disposition."

The king said: "It is not fitting for us to mix with you, Ayladh, since you killed Irakhat."

Ayladh said: "Four things do not mix with one another: night and day; the innocent and the guilty; light and darkness;[15] and goodness and evil."[16]

The king said: "No one should ever trust you, Ayladh."

Ayladh said: "Four are not to be trusted: the thief; the liar; the hypocrite; and the grudging authority."

The king said: "When I see sixteen thousand women and Irakhat is not among them, my sadness increases!"

Ayladh said: "Four are the women for whom no one has the right to be sad: the clumsy woman who is bold with her husband; the flighty, loose, and thieving woman who goes off with whatever he entrusts to her; the heedless one who has neither wealth nor merit; and she who disagrees with her husband, and has an evil and disobedient character."

The king said: "Sadness has never befallen me as in the case of Irakhat, and her good sense."

Ayladh said: "Five are the women for whom one should be sad: the illustrious woman of high breeding; the intelligent, gentle, knowing, patient, and beautiful woman; the brilliant, striking, sincere, and obedient woman; the chaste woman of lucky omen; and she who is obedient to her husband, and pleasing and considerate towards him."

The king said: "Whoever restores Irakhat to me will have all the wealth he desires!"

Ayladh said: "Five love wealth more than themselves: he who fights as a mercenary with no other motive in fighting than obtaining his hire; the thief who breaks into a house or holds some one up on the highway, so that his hand is cut off or he is killed; the merchant who travels at sea seeking to gather ⟨material⁹⁾⟩ wealth; the warden of a prison¹⁷ who wants more people in jail so he can profit from them; ⟨and the judge⁹⁾⟩ who receives bribes in a lawsuit."

The king said: "You maintain that I am bearing you a grudge because you killed Irakhat, Ayladh."

Ayladh said: "Four bear a grudge against each other: the wolf and the lamb; the cat and the mouse; the hawk and the quail; and the owl and the crow."

The king said: "You ruined ⟨my life⁹⁾⟩, Ayladh, the time you killed Irakhat."

Ayladh said: "Seven ruin their works: the devout man versed in the law who is neither well-known nor famous enough for things to be spread abroad or learned through him; the king who grants recognition to every lying, rude turncoat who comes to him; the crude master who has no mercy and does not stop abusing his servants; the mother who treats a bad and dissolute son well, overlooking and forgiving it in him and never reproving him; and the man who, because of his trusting nature, trusts a crafty, wheedling person; he who is quick to blame his friend; and he who heeds neither God nor religious and upright folk."

The king said: "My sadness for Irakhat hinders my sleeping."

Ayladh said: "Six do not sleep: he who is worried about the blood he has shed; wealthy persons who can trust nobody; he who spins slander and libel about people because he is eager for social standing; he who has borrowed much money without any security; the dissolute woman; and he who loves a friend and fears to be separated from him."

The king said:[18] "Have you no mercy? Have mercy on me, Ayladh!"

Ayladh said: "Five have no mercy: the king who holds a grudge and talks nonsense; he who carries dead men for hire 'from their heirs[KF]; the thief who watches for nightfall in order to waylay people and rob them; the manhunter in his pursuit of mischief; and the bold man who disregards whether a thing is his own or not, and loses his own soul and other's in search of what he wants."[19]

The king said: "Really I loathe the killing of Irakhat!"

Ayladh said: "Seven things are loathsome: old age which does away with youth and beauty; suffering which wears down the body and exhausts the blood; anger which ruins the wisdom of the wise and the judgment of the judges; worry which spoils intelligence and wastes the body; cold which injures;[20] hunger and thirst which both weary and humiliate everything; and death which destroys all mankind."

The king said: "You did away with Irakhat and killed her wrongfully, Ayladh."

Ayladh said: "Eight things are wrong: the king who is not just, for his power is wrongful; wise men who do not work according to their knowledge, so that their work is wrong; the miser hoarding the sun and the moon, for hoarding them is wrong; criminals who commit crimes, for their crimes are wrong; the quarrelsome woman, for her tongue is wrongful; mentioning the law to Brahmans, for mentioning the law to them is wrong; and for highway patrolmen and hunters, sleeping is wrong."

The king said: "I can have nothing to do with you after this deed, Ayladh."

Ayladh said: "Eight are not fit to have anything to do with: he who consults an impartial man; he whose heart is not steadfast in a single matter; he who is over-pleased with himself; the liar who is only concerned with his own opinion; he who prefers wealth ahead of himself; the weak individual who embarks upon strange labors; he who is blameworthy in his way of living; and he who is always quarrelsome and argumentative with his friends."

The king said: "Your account, Ayladh, has made me doubt my administration; 'I believe you are doing so in order to test me⁹⁾'."

Ayladh said: "Men ought to be tested in ten things: the brave man in battle; the plowman in plowing;²¹ the slave is tested by his master in society to find out how he gets along with people; the king in the midst of anger tests his patience, knowledge, and intelligence; the merchant in his dealings proves his sincerity and honesty through give and take; brothers prove themselves by how they allow their brethren to annoy them; the prudent man is tested in a calamity which tests his prudence and sympathy; the ascetic is tested in his godliness; the generous man in his giving and mercifulness and compassion; and the poor man is tested by how he shuns crime and seeks sustenance among lawful things."

The king said: "How do you open your mouth in my presence, while you see my displeasure, Ayladh?"

Ayladh said: "Seven people are always displeased: the king who is quick to anger, narrow-minded, and not easy-going; the easy-going person who has no knowledge to match his easy-going manner; the knowing individual who does not desire righteousness; he who desires righteousness without being knowing; the judge who loves bribery; he who is merciful towards men, while he is stingy with his property; and the generous man who seeks a reward and thanks in this life."

The king said: "Indeed you have cheated both yourself and me, Ayladh."

Ayladh said: "Eight cheat themselves and others. He who has little knowledge and undertakes to teach many people. The important man who is intelligent and does not know prudence. He who seeks what he cannot and should not attain. The depraved debauchee who is the worst of those around him and feels in his mind that he can dispense with the advice of respectable and intelligent folk who have been sincere towards him. He who wants to hoodwink kings and important people without rhyme or reason. Whoever seeks knowledge, wanting to argue about it with someone who knows more than himself, and thus does not really accept what is being taught him. He who has dealings with kings without showing them sincerity and the loving devotion of his heart. And the king whose steward and chamberlain are liars and chatterboxes, and are thus ill-disposed and unwilling to accept correction from a teacher."

Then Ayladh was silent. He realized that the king's grief for Irakhat was great, and how he longed for a sight of her; so he said:

"I am right in bringing the king this person whom he loves so dearly and is so eager to see. He has borne many things from me with long-suffering, and I have taken liberties in talking to him without being punished. Indeed there is no king on earth quite like you, nor equal to you in the past or even in the future, since anger did not deprive you of your forebearance, while I was so petty and small-minded in saying what I did. But you were always calm and dignified, as well as having poise in your knowledge and forebearance, and gentleness in treating peace-loving and good people.

"If misfortune should befall you because of the ill-favor of the stars, while God deals you something repulsive and damaging in some critical affair which may force your hand, do not fret about it nor be distraught; but console yourself and show satisfaction and pleasure in whatever it may be.

"Indeed, anyone who is not of your origin and does 'not^(Sp)' behave in his kingdom with vision and greatness, is annihilated, humiliated, and degraded. And if he is one of those who approach you and act favorably, and then carry on your administration in a sly fashion, remove him from office and send him far away! When you have done this and separated what was his from what was yours, he will become anxious and fret about it. Anxiety does not benefit nor satisfy them, but their sadness and worry is increased by anxiety as with misfortune.

"But you, O king, through the nobility of your origin and your abundant patience, controlled yourself and bore what you heard from me, although my manner was petty and my condition weak. So I thank 'God first, then^(Sp)' you, O king, that you did not order me killed, and that I am standing here before you.

"I acted as I did because of my concern and love for you. If I

have thereby been rebellious, I have given you reason and authority to punish and slay me. 'Know, sire^{Sp}, that Irakhat is alive$^{Y/CeD}$,
and I refrained from killing her for fear that you would repent her
death, and would harm me on that account$^{Sp)}$.'"

When the king heard that Irakhat, the mother of Jawir, was
alive, he rejoiced and said to Ayladh: "What prevents me from
becoming angry with you is what I know of your sound advice and
the honesty of your story. I was hoping from my knowledge of
your forebearance that you had not killed Irakhat. For though she
came at me harshly and talked rudely to me, still she did not do
that through spite nor seeking to injure me; but she did it through
jealousy. I ought to have overlooked that and put up with it, and
not become angry, for I know that I was at fault.

"'But you, Ayladh, wanted to test me and leave me in doubt
about her case^{y}. You feared that I would punish you if you said: 'I
did not kill her.' God forbid that such were my idea and that I
might have done that to you! But you deserve to be thanked all the
same. Go fetch me Irakhat, and bring her back to me!"

So Ayladh left the king's presence and ordered Irakhat to adorn
herself and to put on her clothes. So she did so. Then he went off
with her to the king.

When the king saw her, his joy increased, and he said: "Do
what you wish, for I shall never again disregard your whim about
anything."

Irakhat said: "May God prolong your reign with Ayladh! How
would you have come to regret what you had against me the way
you did, if it had not been for your compassion and abundant
patience? For if you had not remembered me until after eternity, I
well deserved having the king kill me for how I acted.

"And Ayladh added to your clemency by refraining from killing
me. If it had not been for Ayladh's trust in your abundant
patience, along with his compassion, equity, and fidelity, he would
have carried out that sentence and killed me."

The king said to Ayladh: "You have benefitted me so much that
it is necessary to thank you for what no king would ever see in
any of his servants. You never did me a greater favor than in not
killing Irakhat; rather you have brought her back to life after I had
killed her! Since you granted her and returned her to me today, I
have never been more pleased with you than I am now. 'You

are entrusted with my kingdom, so do with it as you like!"[Y-C&D]

Ayladh said: "I am your slave, and all I ask today is that you will not be hasty from now on in any important matter which you may come to regret and whose consequences, as you have seen, may cause sadness. Especially in this affair, the like of which has never been found on earth."

The king said: "You have spoken rightly, Ayladh, and I accept your word in everything you command. Why [not] in as important affair like this, which has just occurred to me? From now on I shall never take action in anything great or small except after conferring and reflecting and proceeding deliberately."

Then the king had Irakhat given 'Kuraqanah's[Y-C&D] clothes, and after that the king entered his wives' quarters happy and cheerful.

Later on he and Ayladh conferred about killing those who had wanted to destroy the king's household and family. To they were slain, or stripped of their goods, and banished from the country.

The king and the grandees of his kingdom were consoled, and he praised God and lauded Him. He thanked Kenan Abzun for his excellent knowledge and abundant patience, since his knowledge was instrumental in securing the king's salvation, along with his wives, children, and upright ministers, whom he loved for their attitude towards him.

This is the chapter on forbearance,
intelligence, and good
breeding.

Here Ends the Chapter of Ayladh, Shadram, and Irkhat.

Chapter VIII
The Chapter
of the Cat and the Mouse
[or How To Use Your Enemies][1]

HE KING SAID: "I have understood the fable about one who is hasty in business and does not act with deliberation. Now if you see fit, make me up the fable of a man with many enemies who beset him from all sides so that he is at the point of perishing, and seeks a way out with the help of one of his foes. By becoming reconciled to him, he is saved from what he feared, and repays the one he made peace with. Tell me when one should become reconciled, and how to know it."

The philosopher said: "Enmity and friendship, affection and hatred, are not always permanent and lasting; much affection changes to hatred and much hatred changes to affection, according to circumstances and conditions. The sensible person derives from every happening 'new ideas; when he is faced with an enemy he is severe, and when faced with a friend he is pleasant".

"The intelligent person is not hindered by the enmity he holds against his foe from approaching him and seeking what he can offer, in his eagerness to avert some threat or 'attract" whatever he covets; in fact, he utilizes his judgment in bringing about a meeting and in making up.

"Whoever considers that opinion and accepts it resolutely, overcomes his need. An example of that is of the cat and the mouse who became reconciled: both had sense, and therein lay their salvation and escape from a serious plight."

The king said: "How was that?"

Bidpai the philosopher said:

ONCE UPON A TIME in such and such a place there was a lofty tree. At its foot lay the lair of a wildcat called Rumi, and the hole of a mouse called Qaridun. Hunters often used to hunt game and birds near that tree, and a hunter set his snares and Rumi fell into them. .

The mouse came out searching for something to eat, all the while being on his guard and looking right and left. When he saw the cat caught in the snare, he was glad. Then he looked around behind him and noticed a weasel was stalking him; and he looked above him, and beheld an owl watching him from a tree. He was afraid that if he hurried back, the weasel would spring upon him; and if he dodged right or left, the owl would snatch him up; while if he advanced, the cat lay ahead of him.

So he said 'to himself $^{Y/CeD}$: "This trial is besetting me, and these evils are appearing to me; I have no refuge except in my own intelligence and wits. My object is not to become bewildered nor to let my spirits desert me; for the intelligent individual does not let his judgment get confused, nor overlooks his intelligence in such a situation.

"Intelligent, courageous men are like the sea whose bottom cannot be sounded; while misfortune never causes a sensible person who exerts his intelligence to perish. Neither should hope carry him away and make him vain and giddy, so that his affair seems confused."

Then he added: "There is no trick I can expect to work except trying to make friends with the cat, for the cat has fallen into a similar scrape and perhaps I can free him. Maybe he will listen to what I have to tell him, speaking as a real friend who is not deceitful. If he appreciates my effort and is eager for my assistance, perhaps it will mean salvation for us both."

Then he approached the cat and said: "How are you?"

The civet replied: "Like anyone who has fallen into a jam and a tight spot!"

The mouse said: "Indeed upon my life if you aren't! Still your ill luck delights me, for your tight spot is to my advantage: today I am your partner in misery, and don't expect to be freed except by helping you escape. That is why I am turning to you; so understand that what I say has neither falsehood nor deceit.

"You see where the weasel is lurking for me, and where the owl is waiting to snatch me? Both of them are your enemies and mine, and they both fear and dread you. So if you promise to protect me if I approach you, then I shall escape both of them, cut your ropes, and free you from what you are in. Rely on what I have told you and trust me, since no people are further from safety than two who are on the same footing and with opposite characters, for neither of them will trust the other.

"So you should trust what I promise you with all my heart, and give in to me. Let me approach you without delay; for the intelligent man does not hinder his work. Be glad that I am living, as I am glad of your existence; each of us will be saved by his companion, like the ship and the mariners: the ship carries the sailors out to sea, while they themselves take the vessel out."

When the cat heard the mouse's speech, he knew that he was telling the truth. He liked it, so he said to the mouse:

"I see that what you say ties in with truth and honesty. I am eager for this reconciliation through which I may expect freedom for myself and you. I'll thank you as long as you live, and reward you the best way possible!"

The mouse said: "When I approach you, and the weasel and the owl see my situation, they will both know that we have made up. So they will go away in despair and I shall begin to gnaw your ropes."

So the mouse started to gnaw at the cat's knots.

The civet felt that he was being slow, and said: "I don't see that you are exerting yourself in cutting my knots; now that you have obtained what you need, you are going back on your promise and slackening in what I need. A noble person should not be slack in his friend's need, once he is able to help himself.

"I was quick to make friends with you, in order to benefit and rescue you from destruction, as you have seen. You ought to protect me now, and not remember the enmity that existed between us both. One piece of kindness should make you forget many acts of bad friendship, for the quickest punishment is that of treachery, perjury, and lying, which strikes him who neither pardons nor forgives, when pardon is besought and begged of him."

The mouse said: "There are two kinds of friends: the earnest and the forced; and both of them seek advantage and guard against being harmed. As for the earnest one, you can act familiarly and work along with him under any circumstances; but with the forced friend, there are circumstances where you can treat him familiarly and circumstances in which you will take precautions and constant security through some remaining tie of his; for you still fear him.

"Most relationships and friendships between creatures are not to seek anything except speedy advantage, or the hope of one. Now I fulfilled what I promised you, but am on my guard lest what forced me to make peace with you should befall me again. For each deed has its season, and what is not done then will produce no result. I am cutting your ropes in good time, but am still leaving one knot as security against you; and I shall not cut it except at the moment I know you will be distracted from me."

So he carried on until just as it was dawning, they both saw the hunter approaching from afar.

The mouse said: "Now comes the place for me to exert myself in cutting your ropes!"

The hunter did not come up until the rat had finished 'cutting the ropes'$^{MS.\ (?)}$, with the cat perturbed and thinking evil thoughts about him. When it was finished, he ran to a tree and climbed it, and the mouse slipped into its hole. The hunter picked up his snare which had been cut up, and he went away disappointed.

The mouse came out from his hole afterwards, and saw the cat from a distance. He was shy of approaching him; so the cat called out:

"O friend, my splendid companion in misery! What keeps you from approaching me so I may reward you for your kindness? Come and do not cut me off from your acquaintance, for whoever accepts a friend and then spoils his friendship is thus deprived of the fruits of friendship, and his brethren despair of profiting from it.

"Indeed, the hand which you proferred me is a hand which will never be forgotten! You should be eager to seek such repayment from me and my friends, and not fear anything from me. Know that whatever I have is yours for the asking."

Then he swore and strove to make him believe what he had said.

So the mouse answered: "Hidden enmity often has the appearance of friendship, and is a more serious danger than open enmity. Whoever does not guard against it falls down like the man who was riding an elephant in heat, and then was overcome by drowsiness and fell under the elephant's feet, so that it trampled and killed him. A friend should only be called a friend when one can expect an advantage from him, and an enemy an enemy from whom one fears harm. For when the intelligent man expects something from his enemy, he shows him friendship, and when he fears harm from a friend, he shows him enmity.

"Haven't you seen how animals act when they follow their mother expecting her milk, and when that is cut off, they abandon her? And how clouds are spread out at times, and disappear at others, and how it rains at times and is withheld at others?

"Thus the intelligent man changes towards his friends and companions as conditions alter and circumstances differ; he drifts away at times and comes closer at others, he is familiar at times and on his guard at others, he is pleased at times and discontented at others, he is patient at times and disapproving at others. Often though, a friend breaks off relations with another friend without fearing any evil from him, for the origin of his dealings with him was not enmity.

"Whenever the origin of his dealings is enmity, however, then friendship is created through attendant needs; when the matter causing that passes off, his dealings revert to their original state, like water which is warmed by fire, and turns cold again as soon as it is lifted off. I have no more dangerous foe than in an enmity like yours after there once was affection and true love, and after we were on familiar and kind terms towards each other.

"Need compelled you and me, forcing us both to be friends and to become reconciled. Now the affair which made you need me and me need you has passed, and with its passing I dread a return of enmity. It is not good for a weak individual to be near a strong enemy, nor an underdog near a powerful foe.

"I don't know whether you need me other than to eat me, and

I don't see any way for me to trust you. For I have learned that a weak enemy is better able to free himself from a strong enemy when he is on his guard and is not deceived by him, than is the stronger when he is deceived by a weak enemy who acts amiably towards him. When an intelligent man needs to use his enemy, he flatters him, displaying affection towards him and showing him how kindly he wants to treat him, when he finds no other way out; and he quickly gets away from him as soon as he can.

"I know that whoever has been worsted through kindness can scarcely make up for his fall, and an intelligent man fulfills whatever he has promised to anyone he has made up with, without trusting anything similar in anyone. He intends to get rid of his enemy as soon as he is in a position to do so.

"Your getting away from the hunters and my getting away from you was the best idea. I am fond of you at a distance, and you need not feel you must reward me for any such thing, for there is no way for us to get together."

THUS THE MOUSE BEGAN TO BEWARE OF THE CAT AND TO BE VERY CHARY.

This is the chapter of someone who watches
for his opportunity to become reconciled
with his enemy, and still takes
precautions against him.

Thus Ends the Chapter of the Cat and the Mouse.

Chapter IX

of King Brahmun and Fanzah the Bird
[or Don't Get Stung Twice][1]

HE KING said to the philosopher: "I have heard the fable about the man surrounded by enemies, who asks help from and makes friends with one of them, so that he is freed from what he feared and is saved. So if you see fit, make me up a fable about troublesome people whom one ought to avoid."

The philosopher said:

ONCE UPON A TIME there lived a certain king named Brahmun, who had a bird called Fanzah. It was talkative and shrewd, and had a chick. The king ordered Fanzah and his chick both kept in a place with the lady who was his chief wife, and he ordered her to 'watch over'$^{Y/CeD)}$ them both. His wife bore a boy, and the chick got used to the lad and they began to play together.

Now every day Fanzah used to go off to the mountain and bring home two of the most succulent fruits 'which nobody knew'$^{Y/CeD)}$. He used to feed one of them to his chick and the other to the king's son. That hastened their growth and strength, until the king realized it and increased in his respect for Fanzah.

Then one day when Fanzah was absent in search of fruit, his chick sprang into the boy's bird cage, and made the boy angry. He seized the chick at that, and threw it on the ground and killed it.

When Fanzah came home and saw his chick killed, he became sad, and cried and said:

"Shame on kings who do not keep their word nor honor their

friends! No one has any protection against them, nor is he honored unless they are eager for some profit or advantage. When they have used him they no longer feel any tie of friendship nor reward any show of kindness, nor forgive any fault; but their aim is only to earn money, be immoral, and let on[2] that every serious crime they commit is petty and rests lightly on them. Today I shall avenge myself on the unmerciful ingrate and his deceitful wretch of a companion and partner, his playmate and tablemate."

Thus he sprang at the boy's face and clawed out his eyes. Then he flew away and perched upon a lofty place, sad at heart.

The news reached the king, and he was extremely upset. He tried to think up some way of overcoming Fanzah. So he rode up and stopped by him, calling him by name and saying:

"You can trust me, so come here!"

Fanzah refused and said: "O king, the traitor has been caught by his treachery. If the hasty punishment of this world misses its mark, that of the next will not go astray, so that punishment will overtake his offspring and his children's offspring. Your son betrayed me, and I dealt him his punishment (in this world[3])."

The king said: "Upon my life, we did that to you; while you have avenged yourself upon us. We have nothing on you, nor have you any way of retaliation against us. So return to us in confidence!"

Fanzah said: "I am not returning to you, for the prudent person refrains from approaching a wronged man. They say: A rancorous man's kindness, meekness, and esteem will only increase with his feeling of fury towards you; so you won't find any safer way of trusting a rancorous and wronged man, but by dreading, keeping your distance, and being on your guard against him.

"And it has been said: The intelligent man counts his parents only as friends, his brothers as companions, his wives as a pastime, sons as namesakes, daughters as troublemakers, kinsfolk as debtors, and he reckons himself as quite alone. And I am quite alone, having been furnished with a heavy burden of sadness which no one will carry for me. Thus I am going away; and so, good-bye!"

The king said: "If you weren't satisfied with what we did for you, or your action had been other than a betrayal, the matter would be as you mention. But since we are off to such a bad start through no fault of yours, what hinders you from trusting us? Return and be confident!"

Fanzah said: "Grudges leave painful and sore spots in one's heart, and the tongue does not speak the truth about the heart: the heart testifies more honestly about itself than the tongue. In fact, I know that my heart does not testify about your tongue, nor does your heart about my tongue."

The king said: "Don't you know that people have numerous rancors and grudges? A person with intelligence is skeptical of bearing grudges and is eager to guard against them."

Fanzah said: "That is as you say, and the sensible person should not think that one who bears him a grudge for having been wronged, is a person who will wrong him and then go away. The sensible man will dread snares and trickery, and he understands that many enemies are not overcome by violence and bullying, so that they are hunted with gentleness and courtesy, just as the wild elephant is hunted with the tame elephant."

The king said: "The high-minded man does not abandon his friendship and cut off his brethren nor ruin his memory, even if he fears for himself. We already know that people slaughter 'cattle^{Sp}[3] and eat them, while the 'cattle^{Sp}' see them often, since they have become tame, and their very tameness prevents them from leaving them."

Fanzah said: "Grudges are to be feared whenever they occur. The most fearful and serious are what kings harbor, for kings profess the custom of revenging themselves, and consider a chance for retaliation as a noble and glorious action.

"The intelligent man ought not to be deluded by a lull in rancor, for rancor dormant in the heart is similar to embers which have cooled off since there is no more firewood for them: rancor always seeks excuses, as fire desires fuel; and when it finds its excuse, it is kindled as fire is kindled. It is not quenched by water or words, by gentleness or softness, by submissiveness or pleading, nor by anything else than the person in question.

"Nevertheless someone with a grudge is often anxious to associate with the one he hates, for he hopes that he may thus be able to use him or to pay him back. But I am weaker 'than you, so you cannot find any help or advantage in me^{Sp}'; so I should remove what you have on your mind. If your feelings are as you say, that has nothing to do with me, for I shall always fear and have bad thoughts about you so long as we keep company, and there is no opinion besides separating from you and wishing you well."

The king said: "You know that it is impossible for one person to harm or benefit another, for nothing large or small strikes anyone except through preordained fate. Thus the creation of whatever is created and begot, and however long it endures, is not a concern of creatures themselves. Likewise with the perishing or passing away of whatever passes away.

"What you did to my son is not your fault, nor is my son to blame for the demise of your chick: that was predestined fate, to which we all are subject. Let us not blame what fate has brought you, 'for if I intend to take and kill you, while God's judgment is against what I want, you cannot do anything about it.℗'."

Fanzah said: "Fate is as you mention; but that does not prevent a resolute man from taking precautions against something he fears, or guarding against someone he should guard against. Rather he unites the truth of fate with his own share of strength and resolve.

"I know that you are telling me other than what is on your mind, for what stands between you and me is that your son killed my chick, and that I put out your son's eyes. Now you want to kill me by fooling me, while I refuse to die!

"It has been said that destitution is a trial, sadness is a trial, 'being near one's enemy is a trial℗', separation from loved ones is a trial, disease is a trial, and 'old age$^{Y/CeD}$ is a trial; while the chief trial of them all is the trial of death.

"And there is no one who knows better what is on the mind of an afflicted and worried man than he who has experienced the same thing. I know what is on your mind from my own example; your company is no good for me since you will never recall what I did to your son, nor I what your son did to my chick, without it causing our hearts to alter."

The king said: "Whoever cannot overlook what is on his mind and try to forget it, is no good. He will stifle it so that he does not remember anything and there is no room for it in his mind."

Fanzah said: "A man who has a sore on the sole of his foot, finds that walking is impossible even if he wants to be nimble, because of the chafing. And a bleary-eyed man only exposes his eye to irritation when he faces the wind. Likewise when a wronged man approaches his enemy, he allows his feelings to be hurt, for the worldly person is not able to guard against ruination and to determine matters except by relying upon his own strength and cunning, and rarely overlooking what is untrustworthy. Yet he who relies upon his own strength is undertaking to travel along dangerous roads and to work towards his own demise.

"Whoever cannot stand what he eats and drinks often kills himself by forcing what should not be forced down his throat. And whoever cannot judge a morsel and pops it right into his mouth without being able to swallow it, chokes on it and dies. Whoever is heedless and is put off his guard by 'his enemy's[Y/CtD] word, is more his own enemy 'than his enemy himself[Sp)].

"A man should not be on his guard when he does not know what fate will bring him or keep from him, but he should act resolutely, conduct himself staunchly, and give a good account of himself in his business. The intelligent man does not fear anyone unnecessarily, nor keep on fearing him, but he finds some other way out. I have so many ways out that I do not expect to turn anywhere without finding what will profit me.

"There are five qualities which provide one with his needs anywhere he may be, brings closer what is distant, makes him feel at home while he is abroad, and procures him a living and friends: 'first[Y CtD], refraining from harming anyone; 'second[Y/CtD], fine breeding; 'third[Sp)], avoiding suspicion; 'fourth[Sp)], a generous character; and 'fifth[Sp]meritorious[n] conduct. When an intelligent being fears for himself, he willingly gives up family, children, country, and wealth, since he expects compensation for all that, and does not hope for any compensation in himself.

"The worst form of wealth is that which is not marketable, the worst of wives is she who does not obey her husband, the worst of children is the rebellious one, the worst of brethren is the one who forsakes 'his friend in the hour of trouble[Y/CtD], the worst of kings is he who is feared by innocent people, and the worst of countries is the land wherein no one is to be trusted. I have no trust in you, and there is no tranquility for my soul so long as I am near you!"

Then he took his leave of the king and flew away.

This is the fable of troublesome people who are on their guard against each other.

Here Ends the Chapter of the King and Fanzah the Bird.

Chapter X
The Chapter
of the Lion and the Fasting Jackal
[or the Reconciliation of Friends][1]

HE KING said to the philosopher: "The fable about troublesome people who are on their guard one against the other has been understood. So if you see fit, make me up a fable about what happens between kings and their intimates, and how one is returned to favor after punishment or ill-treatment which had occurred through some fault committed or harm inflicted [against him]."

The philosopher said: "If the king does not restore someone who has been treated badly or punished because of a crime committed or injury done [to him], then it damages the former's administration and actions. A king ought to look into the state of someone who has experienced a thing like that and test him for his kindness and whatever advantage he can expect from him.

"If he is able to profit from and rely upon him for his judgment and loyalty, the king is right in soliciting his return; for a king is unable to do anything except with ministers and deputies. Neither can he use his ministers and assistants except with affection and sincerity, and there is no sincerity nor affection without keen wits and much self-restraint.

"For a king's works are many and$^{Y/CeD)}$ need 'many workers$^{Y/CeD}$ and helpers$^\eta$', and those who combine what I have mentioned of sound advice and sharp wits are few. He must hold resolutely to whatever controls matters, provided the king is conscious of the affection of his prospective assistant, and how solicitous or sensible each man is and what sort of defect he has.

"When he has settled that from his own knowledge and the knowledge of someone he trusts and who helps him straighten [his things out], he appoints to each office someone he needs and who he knows is steadfast, courageous, and sensible; while he guards against considering for a post where manliness is not needed, one who has it, nor trusting his defects and other consequences which may have an ugly twist.

"It is the king's further duty to keep on close terms with his deputies and to watch them and whatever they do; so that the good and evil deeds they may perform are not concealed from him.

"Then after that, they must not leave any efficient person without a reward, nor retain any evil-doer or inefficient individual in his inefficiency or evil-doing; for by acting in this way they overlook the well-doer and hearten the evil-doer, spoiling administration and ruining work. That fable is the fable of the lion and the jackal."

The king said: "What is that?"

The philosopher said:

ONCE UPON A TIME in such and such a country 'of India^{Y/CeD)} there lived a jackal who was godly and chaste, abstaining from the company of she-jackals and foxes and wolves. He did not act as they acted, nor went raiding as they raided, nor shed blood and ate flesh.[2]

Those beasts reprimanded him and said: "We are not pleased with your way of life, nor your opinion that you are devoting yourself to God. Your devotion to God won't gain you anything since you can't act like one of us, carrying on with us and doing what we do. There is no reason to withhold your hand from bloodshed and abandon meat."

The jackal said: "My companionship with you does not entail any sin for me when I do not sin myself: sins do not belong to one's place and companions, but to the heart and one's actions. If a person lived in a holy place then his work would be holy, and a person living in an evil place would be evil in his action; when someone killed a hermit in his cell, he would not sin, and whoever survived a battlefield would sin. Don't you see that your companion-ship with me is nothing but a companionship in (body$^{\Psi}$) and not in deed, for I know the fruit of your actions?"

Meanwhile the jackal continued as he was and became known as an ascetic and accomplished in judgment. Thus it reached the lion, who was king of the beasts in that region; and he longed to know him because of what he had heard about his chastity, truthfulness, and loyalty. So he sent for him, and spoke to him and tested him.

Then some days later, he summoned him to keep him company, saying:

"My kingdom is great, my duties are heavy, and I need helpers. Now it had reached me how intelligent and abstemious you are; then I met you and wanted to know you even more. I am your right-hand man, and shall promote you ahead of the nobles and name you one of my officials."

The jackal said: "Kings are right in (testing$^{Y/CeD)}$) their helpers, and in taking care in their administration and affairs lest anyone take a dislike to his work and not be capable of exerting himself at it. I dislike the work of ruling and have had no experience in it, nor in dealing with a sovereign. You are king of the beasts and have a great number of all kinds of beasts, amongst them people of sagac-ity and strength, eager to work, and sympathetic. If you use them, they will serve you well and be content with whatever they attain."

The lion said: "Stop talking like this, for I am not exempting you from office!"

The jackal said: "Only two men are capable of friendship with a ruler, (and I am not$^{Y/CeD)}$) one of them: either a fawning liar who offers whatever is needed and keeps on the safe side with his flattery; or else the servile man who is so ignored that no one envies him.

"As for someone who wants to keep company with a sovereign properly, honestly, and decently and not get mixed up with flat-tery, their company is rarely safe for him since the sovereign's ene-mies and friends both join in envying and hating him. A friend will vie with him in rank and wrong him just like an enemy; while the ruler's enemy will brood against him for his honesty and good ser-vice to the ruler, so that when both groups unite against him, he will be exposed to destruction."

The king said: "Don't let the injustice and envy (of my friends^{n})

cause you to talk about your worries, since I shall protect you and concede you honor and kindness for your trouble."

The jackal said: "If the king wants to treat me well and honor me, then let me live on in this wilderness, trusting that I shall be satisfied with a living off water and grass. For I know that a ruler's companion receives more harm and anxiety in one hour than another receives in ⟨all his life$^{Y/CeD}$⟩; and a meagre life in trusting and tranquility is better than an ample one in fear and toil."

The lion said: "I have heard what you have to say, so don't fear a thing of what I see you are afraid of, for I can do nothing except help you."

The jackal said: "Inasmuch as the king insists, then will he make a covenant with me that if one of his companions should treat me unjustly for fear I should assume his superior rank, or if someone lower than myself contends for my rank and, speaking for himself or for somone else, tells the king whatever he likes in order to turn your majesty against me, that he will not proceed hastily, but make certain concerning whatever point is raised against me and investigate it.

"After that, the king may dispose of me as he sees fit. As for myself, when I can rely upon your majesty for that, I shall help him and do for him whatever he may entrust to me sincerely, earnestly, and eagerly, so that there will be no way of attacking me."

The lion said: "I ⟨grant$^{Sp)}$⟩ you that."

So he placed him in charge of his treasury, and asked his advice and judgment about his household more often than that of his other companions. His admiration for him increased daily, and he rose in honor and offices, so that it oppressed those around the lion, such as his intimates, companions, and officials. They treated him as an enemy and envied him, and they consulted together about turning the lion against him and destroying him.

When they had agreed upon what sort of trick they would use, one day they hid the meat which the lion had just procured and enjoyed. He had ordered it put away with his other food, so that he could have it again; so they stole it. They sent it to the jackal's house and hid it in such a way that no one could discover it. ⟨Then^{Y} they assembled in the lion's presence$^{Y/CeD}$ to lie about him when the opportunity would arise$^{)}$⟩.

Next day when the lion called for his breakfast and missed that meat, he demanded it and did not find it. The jackal was absent, and the faction in favor of fraud and deceit was present. So the lion mustered them out in search of the meat. Finally he became quite angry, and some of them nodded to the others.

One of them said, as if he were giving sincere advice: "There is nothing for us to do but inform the king about whatever we know, whether it will harm or benefit him, or even if it should grieve him. It has reached me that the jackal went off home with that meat."

Another said: "'I don't see'[n] how he would do this; but search and investigate, for it is important to know one's fellow creatures."

Another said: "Upon my life, no one discovers very much about secrets, for if you investigate and find that 'meat'[Y/CeD], then everything which has been mentioned to us concerning his shortcomings and trickery is true, and we will be right in forsaking him and judging him by all that has been said about him."

Another said: "It is not necessary for anyone to be deceived when he himself knows about a fraud, for a fraud does not save its perpetrator nor remain hidden."

Another said: "How is anyone saved who defrauds a ruler, and how is that hidden? A fraud upon friends is never hidden!"

Another said: "Indeed I was told a serious matter about the jackal which didn't strike my attention until I heard your words."

Another said: "As for me, his business and trickery were never hidden from me, since I saw them from the start and said so many times. I have So-and-so for witness that this impostor puts on humble airs and looks at us as if the work entrusted to him were a trial and that this breach of trust were only an accident—indeed, the strangest thing possible!—'While he was only living in falsehood and sin[Sp]."

Another said: "If this is found out to be right, it is not only trickery, but also ingratitude for favors received and boldness to the point of sinning."

Another said: "You are people of fairplay and excellence, and you cannot lie; but to distinguish the truth from the falsehood in this matter, why doesn't the king send to the jackal's house and search it?"

Another said: "If his dwelling is to be inspected, then hurry up, for his spies and scouts are scattered everywhere!"

Another said: "Indeed, I know that if the jackal has his dwelling searched and his knavery discovered, he will contrive some deal or trick to cast doubt in the king's mind, so that he will pardon and let him off."

They did not stop talking in this and other ways until their suspicions about the jackal penetrated the lion's mind; so he called him and said to him:

"What did you do with the meat I ordered you to keep?"

He said: "I delivered it to So-and so, the steward, so that he could prepare it for the king."

The king summoned the steward, who was one of those in league with the faction, and asked him about the meat.

He answered: "He didn't deliver anything to me."

So the king sent his trusted men to inspect the jackal's lodgings. They found the meat there, and brought it to him.

Then the lion was approached by a wolf who had not spoken about any of these matters, and who seemed to be for fairplay. He never talked about anything except what seemed quite proper; and he said to the lion:

"Once the king has discovered the jackal's trickery, then do not pardon him! For if he is pardoned, then no one will reveal a trickster's fraud nor a criminal's crime to the king again."

So the lion ordered the jackal taken out and placed under guard until he came to a decision about him.

Meanwhile one of the lion's councilors said: "I am surprised at the lion's opinion, with his knowledge of affairs. How was this matter hidden from him? He didn't know anything about his deceitfulness and imposture!"

Another said: "I'll be amazed if I don't see him giving it thought after what he has seen."

Then the lion ⌈got angry and[Sp]⌉ sent one of them to the jackal to ask him for some explanation. He returned from the jackal with a falsified message, and the lion became so angry that he ordered the jackal to be executed.

The lion's mother[3] heard about that, and she realized that the lion was acting hastily in this affair. So she asked those who had been ordered to kill him to postpone it, and she went to her son and said:

"For what crime have you ordered the jackal executed?"

The lion informed her about the matter.

She said: "Aren't you acting hastily, my son? The intelligent man saves himself from regret by abandoning hasty action and being sure of himself. 'For the fruit of haste is repentance$^{(Y)}$. Resolute action is for kings, as the wife is for the husband, the child for the parents, the pupil for the teacher, the army 'for$^{Y(CeD)}$ the captain, the ascetic for religion, the people for kings, kings for the fear of God, the fear of God for intelligence, and intelligence for resolute action.

"And the chief resolve of a king is to know his companions, assigning them to their places and watching some with others; for if one of them finds a way to destroy his companion, to slander the zeal of the zealous, and the good works of the well-doer, and to conceal the evil deeds of the evil-doer, he will not stop at anything. This quickly leads to spoiling and upsetting matters, and brings about serious damage and loss.

"You had already tested the jackal and been informed about his breeding and virtue before you asked his help and appointed him; and I have always been pleased with that. As the days pass, my pleasure and kindness and regard for him only increase. And so you ordered him killed for a side of meat you have lost!

"It is easy for his companions to have blamed him criminally and falsely because of their envy and to help one another against him. You know that when kings entrust others with what they ought to work on themselves, and assign to themselves what they should hand over to competent persons, their administration is ruined. And they bring down ruination upon themselves.

"Kings need to look into the appearance of diverse matters, and when they choose some aspects ahead of others, they must be sure they are not making any mistake in observation nor any error in judgment; just as the wine merchant who wants to make a purchase needs to test it for its color, flavor, and odor. For if he tests for only part of them, he is never sure of not being cheated and misled.

"And he is like a man who sees something like a hair between his eyes because of some illness afflicting him, and he cannot ascertain whether it is a hair or not; for he knows that if it is, another person would have noticed it the same as he, so that he could make certain and think about his illness. It is like the firefly which an ignorant man sees in the dark, and decides it is fire by seeing it before he touches it; then when he touhes it, he clearly perceives his error in judgment.

"You were right in looking into the jackal's case, for you know that when he has not eaten meat which you have often ordered him to keep in even larger quantities, and has been preparing food for you and your court, he is incapable of filching the little bit of meat which you ordered him to store. Investigate his case, for it is always the custom of wicked villains to envy virtuous and understanding people, and harm and busy themselves about them.

"The jackal is virtuous and understanding, and it is easy for his enemies among your companions to have arranged to put that meat in his lodgings without his knowing it. For if a hawk clutches a piece of meat, many other birds will vie for it. And when a dog seizes a bone and is holding it in his mouth, a number of dogs will band together against him.

"If you haven't noticed the jackal's enemies among your companions, then look for them yourself and don't pay any attention to them, since they are urging you to injure yourself. The most serious things for people in general and for rulers in particular are two matters: that they should be deprived of honest helpers and ministers and friends; and that their ministers and friends should be unmanly and inefficient.

"The jackal's efficiency has always been important to you: he has preferred your profit to his pleasure, and has purchased your peace of mind with his own advantage, and your contentment with the displeasure of your associates. He has never concealed any secret nor hidden any matter from you; he did not see anything without enduring it instead of you, or attending to it no matter how serious it might be. What associate has this trait, which ranks on the same level as fathers, sons, and brothers?"

While the lion's mother was in conversation, one of those who had plotted against the jackal entered and informed the king 'that the jackal was innocent'$^{Y/CeD)}$.

When the lion's mother learned that the lion had been informed of the jackal's innocence, she said to him: "Now that you are informed of your companions' boldness and their ganging up on him, don't be satisfied with knowing just that; keep breaking up their plot until you have blocked all compassion for them so they will never take you as a tool again. Accustom them to bear with your harsh treatment and their own disgrace!

"Do not be fooled by your power, for that will lead you to belittle them and to overlook what they may do. For weak grass when it is joined and plaited, thereby becomes a strong rope which binds a powerful elephant in heat.

"Restore the jackal to his rank and office, and do not despair of his advising you well even after your being so remiss as to treat him badly. One need not fear deceit and enmity from everyone who is wronged, nor despair of his sound advice and affection; but in this case one must appoint people to office in line with their various differences. For there are some whom it is advisable to break off relations with and never go back to, once one has managed to get rid of them; and there are some whom it is not fitting to leave nor separate from under any circumstances.

"Whoever is known for his wicked nature, for breaking his word and seldom keeping his promises, for drunkenness, lack of respect, and not being able to get along with his companions and brethren if he gets no favors from them, should be prevented from further intercourse with people.

"Whoever has none of these defects, and is generous towards the friends he knows, tolerating a disgusting one if he has such, and helping him even if it weighs him down, and is known for his superior godliness and for being happy with whatever events or circumstances may befall him, then one should seize every opportunity to join him and keep from being separated from him. 'You have tested the jackal and know him, wherefore you should love him again[9]'."

So the lion summoned the jackal and begged his pardon, and informed him that he was being returned to his rank and office.

The jackal said: "When one's companion bears whatever his friend has to offer of hardship and adversity which may injure him, and he bears whatsoever he may be confronted with, it is difficult to find the like of him. Let not the king take it amiss if I tell him that he has no way to have any confidence in me, for he ought not to consider me a sound adviser.

"Whoever has been stricken with a serious misfortune without deserving it, being removed from his high station and offices, or is deprived of his wealth wrongfully, or has been close [to his sovereign] and then been banished without cause, or has merited a reward from his peers while someone beneath him is rewarded and preferred ahead of him, or if he is known for his excessive greed and gluttony, or thinks there is harm in his sovereign's advantage, or his own profit in his harm the ruler ought not to commission any of these nor trust them. For all of them must be against him and with his assassins.

"Today it is clearly seen that I have become a target for the king's enemies, and none of the affection and sound advice which I bore the king prevented your majesty from suspecting me and entertaining evil thoughts despite what had happened previously. Neither is the affection and sincere advice I have shown him anything I may rely upon, for I cannot thereby be confident that my enemies will not incite the king against me again through falsehood and lying, anxious lest I requite them and eager that I should not let the king discover the truth of their lying when they incited him against me in the first place. If they do so, they will not require the king to accept any more powerful aid than this suspicion which has already lodged in the king's mind.

"Even so, if your majesty had confidence and little suspicion of me, I would have no other recourse in the straits I find myself in, than to dread his suspicion of the company I keep, his evil thoughts concerning me, and his speech in believing my enemies when they incited him against me.

"For I recall the haste that was used against me. When the king's state of mind in trusting me and my state in trusting him is as it has been described, it is up to him to look for whatever means he can find to make me desire his company."

The lion said: "I tested your habits and traits indeed, and in my mind your rank is with the noblest and the best. The high-minded man forgets a thousand wrongs done him for one kind deed, while the ignoble man forgets a thousand kind deeds for one evil.

"But I am trusting that you will forget what has happened because of our kindness to you, which occurred previous to your affair. Indeed we trust you again, so trust us again in whatever we may offer you, for you will thereby become prosperous and happy."

So the jackal returned to the offices he had handled in the lion's administration, and no day went by in which he was not more useful and prosperous until he passed away. 'And the lion degraded those who had accused him and cast them out of his land into exile$^{)}$.

> This is the chapter of a sovereign's
> ministers, associates,
> and helpers.

Here Ends the Chapter of the Lion and the Fasting Jackal.

Chapter XI

The Chapter

of the Pilgrim and the Goldsmith

[Or Man the Ingrate][1]

HE KING said to the philosopher: "I have heard what you have mentioned to me of kings' administration and what passes between them and their intimates and how one of them may return to favor. Now inform me about whomever a king ought to favor and is right in trusting and whose help can be relied upon."

The philosopher said: "A king as well as others can quite properly do good to those of his people from whom he may hope to receive thanks and praise, and not look towards intimates and their own people nor to nobles, richer and more powerful persons, nor yet refrain from benefitting weak, striving, and lowly people.

"It is sensible that they try out and test the small and the mighty, both in their gratitude and how they return affection, and in their perfidy and ingratitude. Thus their actions will be according to the ability they have observed or is manifested to them.

"For a skillful physician does not tend the sick by merely glancing at them, but he looks at their urine and feels their pulse; then prescribes the cure according to his knowledge and ability. It is right for the keenwitted man, once he has found people who are respectful and grateful, or animals of the same type, that he should act kindly in whatever occurs between them, lest perchance he need them some day in the course of time, and they will requite him the same way.

"The intelligent man is often on his guard against people, and he does not even trust himself. He catches a weasel and brings it into his lodgings, or a bird and places on his wrist. For it has been said: An intelligent person should not look down upon any person great or small, nor on any animal; but he ought to be friendly with them all and do what he can for them insofar as he sees what they amount to.

"In fact, there once was a fable that a certain wise man made up about that."

The king said: "What was that?"

The philosopher said:

Once upon a time some people went off to the wilds and dug a pit for the animals there. So a goldsmith, a tiger,[2] a snake, and a monkey fell into it, and the latter did not get excited about that man in any way.

A pilgrim passed by the pit and looked down into it. When he saw them there, he thought the matter over and said:

"I do not see a more noteworthy deed I can perform for the next world than freeing this man from the midst of his enemies!"

So he took a rope and lowered it to them. The monkey hung onto it because of his nimbleness, and climbed out. Then he returned it a second time, and the tiger clung to it, and he brought him out. Then he went back a third time, and the snake twisted itself about it, and he rescued it.

So they thanked him for his deed, and said: "Don't let this man out and free him, 'because nothing is so ungrateful as man[n].'"

And the monkey added: "My home is by the city called Barajun."

The tiger also said: "I live in a thicket nearby."

And the snake said: "I also live in its wall; so if you come there at some future date or pass by it, and have need of us, call upon us so that we can come and reward you for what you have done and your kindness towards us."

Then the pilgrim lowered the rope to the man who was a goldsmith, not heeding what the monkey, the tiger, and the snake had mentioned to him about his ingratitude; and he helped him out.

The latter thanked him and greeted him, saying: "You have granted me a great boon; and I am right in doing something about it. If you happen to come to the city of Barajun, ask for me, for that is where I live. Perhaps I can repay you some of the service I have experienced from you."

Everyone went his own way, while the pilgrim tarried for some time. Then he happened to need to go to the city, and so he set out for it.

The monkey came out and greeted him. He kissed his hand and his foot, and begged pardon of him, saying:

"I don't own anything, but wait an hour until I fetch you something I may find."

Then he went off and was not long in bringing him some fine fruit. He placed it before him and wished him well.

Then the pilgrim went on towards the city, and he met the tiger. The latter bowed down to him, wished him well, and said:

"You granted me a really big favor, and I'll have no rest until I return it!"

He was not long in doing so, for he went off to the king's daughter, killed her, and took her jewelry. Then he came back and handed it over to [the pilgrim] without his knowing what had occurred.[3]

The pilgrim asked himself: "These animals have granted me all this! How will it be if I go to the goldsmith? For even if he is destitute and has nothing, he will still sell this jewelry for its value, and thus he will give me part of it, and he will keep some."

Then the pilgrim entered the city and proceeded to the goldsmith's. The latter welcomed him and had him come in.

When he caught sight of the jewelry he had with him, he recognized it and said: "Wait till I fetch you some food to eat, for I cannot please you with anything I have in the house!"

So the goldsmith went off to the king's palace[4] and sent a message in to the king declaring: "The man who killed your daughter and took her jewelry has been caught by me, and is a prisoner at my house."

The king sent ʿhis constableᵖʾ for the pilgrim, and he seized him. When he saw the jewelry with him, he ordered him tortured, paraded around the city, and then hanged. When that had befallen him, and he was being paraded around the city he began to cry out and exclaim at the top of his voice:

"If only I had heeded the monkey, the snake, and the tiger, in what they ordered me ⌈and told me about man's ingratitude[Y/CtD]⌉, this plight would never have befallen me!"

When the snake heard what he said, she came out from her hole. When she caught sight of him, he seemed in urgent need of assistance, and she pondered over some scheme to save him.[5]

The snake went off to one of her sisters among the genii and informed her about the case and how that pilgrim had performed such a service for her. Thus the snake won her sympathy; and [at her suggestion] she went off to the king's son and stung him in the foot.

Next, [her sister] ⌈rendering herself invisible[Kn]⌉, went off to the king's son and worked over him. Then she said to him: "Know that you will not recover until this pilgrim who has been maltreated charms you!"

When the king heard about that, he called the wise men to charm him. So they charmed him and did not get anywhere with it. Then they looked at the stars and contrived with him till he spoke and said:

"I shall not recover until this pilgrim is brought to charm me, and touches me with his hands; for the king has ordered him to be executed wrongfully and unjustly."

The snake had [meanwhile] gone off to the pilgrim and informed him about that, saying: "Didn't I warn you against the man, and you did not obey me?"

She gave him a shrub as an antidote for her poison, and told him: "When you meet the king, charm the youth and give him some of this shrub to drink, so that he will recover. Then tell the king the true story so that if God so will it, you may be saved."[6]

Thus after the king had summoned the magicians, he found that they were of no avail. His son then said to him:

"My cure lies with this ascetic whom you have seized and ordered to be tortured."

So the king ordered the ascetic's punishment stopped and had him brought into his presence. When he arrived, he ordered him to charm his son.

⌈So the monk[Sp]⌉ said: "I am unable to charm, but ⌈if he drinks a decoction of these leaves^{Kn)}, I shall say a prayer over him which I hope will cure him."

'The king^{Y/CeD)} said: "I have only called on you so you might tell me what you need."

The pilgrim recounted his case to the king: what he had done for the goldsmith, the tiger, the snake, and the monkey; what they had said to him; and what had induced him to come to the city. Then he said:

"O God, Thou knowest that I am speaking the truth in what I relate, so be speedy in freeing the king's son from what he is suffering, so that he can be cured and recover!"

The lad recovered from what he had, and God released him from it. The king offered the pilgrim gifts and presents, and he treated him kindly; while he ordered the goldsmith to be hanged. And so he was hanged.

Then the philosopher said to the king: "In what the goldsmith did for the pilgrim and his ingratitude towards him after he had been rescued, and the animals' thanks and how one of them saved him, is food for the thoughtful and should be considered by whoever thinks how a favor and kindness are performed for people who pay their debts and are generous, whether near or far. For whatever will make judgment surer, procure good, or get rid of something loathsome, results in service [to humanity].

Here Ends the Chapter of the Pilgrim,
the Goldsmith, the Tiger, the
Monkey and the
Snake.

(The Chapter of the King's Son Begins.)

Chapter XII

The Chapter

of the Four Companions

[or Luck, Looks, Wits, and Toil]

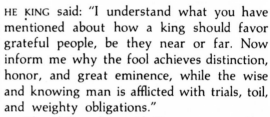HE KING said: "I understand what you have mentioned about how a king should favor grateful people, be they near or far. Now inform me why the fool achieves distinction, honor, and great eminence, while the wise and knowing man is afflicted with trials, toil, and weighty obligations."

The philosopher said: "Just as a man does not see except with his eyes, nor hear except with his ears; likewise knowledge has its fulfillment only in patience, intelligence, and perseverance. Nonetheless, destiny and fate both overcome all that, for they incline their possessor to good times or to destruction.

"The story of that is in the fable of the king's son who was seen sitting by the gate of the city called Matun. After he had completed his business, he wrote upon it: 'Intelligence, beauty, toil, strength, etc., have their basis in destiny and fate.' "

The king said: "How was that?"

The philosopher said:

ONCE UPON A TIME four persons made friends 'on a road$^{Y/C\epsilon D)}$. One of them was the son of a king, the second was the son of a noble, the third the son of a merchant, and the fourth the son of a plowman. They were all needy, and had been afflicted with hardship and distress. They did not own a thing except what they had on in the way of clothes.

While they were walking along ⌈talking together, they started to argue about how things go in this world, and how man can have wealth, pleasure, and enjoyment⌉[Sp].

The king's son said: "The affairs of this world are all according to fate!"

The merchant's son said: "Intelligence is the most distinguished thing of all."[1]

The noble's son said: "Beauty is better than anything you are mentioning."

The peasant's son said: "Toil is more outstanding than all that!"

[A. The Farmer's Son]

Then they passed on towards the city called Matun. When they came near that city, they ⌈sat down⌉[Y/CeD] in its vicinity, and said to the plowman's son:

"Go off ⌈and earn⌉[Y] some food for us with your toil during this day!"

He went off and enquired: "Where is there work which a man may perform from morning till nightfall, so that he may earn the wherewithall to feed a group of four?"

He was told: "There is nothing dearer than kindling, ⌈while firewood is to be found a league away⌉[Sp]."

So he went off there and loaded some of the heavy sort of firewood and sold it for half a dirhem. Then he bought the wherewithall to satisfy his companions, and he wrote on the city wall:

1 DAY'S WORK = ½ DIRHEM

He brought them what he had bought, and they took it from him and made a meal of it.

[B. The Noble's Son]

When they arose in the morning, they said: "⌈Let's cast lots, so that the one on whom the lot falls must go and find out his fortune."

So they cast lots, and it fell[Sp)] to the noble's son, 'who was very handsome and well-built.

They said to him:[Sp)] "Go off with your beauty and earn something for us to eat!

So he went off 'and reached the city[Y/CᵉD] gate.[Sp)] He pondered in his mind, and said: "I am unable to work at anything!"

He was ashamed to return to his companions without any food, and was wondering whether he should separate from them or not. In his quandary, he leaned back against a tree in the city, 'and started to watch the people passing by.[Sp)]

Now a woman whose family was important 'in the city[n] happened to 'ride past on her mule. Her women went after her, along with her servants. She noticed him there, and not recognizing him, she realized that he was a strange man. She saw how handsome and well-built he was, and also how worried, and so she felt sorry for him.

Being taken with his beauty, 'as soon as she reached home,[Sp)] she sent one of her maidservants for him. 'The woman reached him and found him asleep from worry. She woke him up and said:

"My mistress, Madame So-and-So, the wife of Such-and-Such, sends me to you and asks you to come to call on her at home."

He said: "What does your mistress want of me, and why is she sending for me? For she doesn't know who I am nor has any acquaintance with me."

The woman said: "She is wondering about you, and wants to ask about your business and what you're doing, and to show you the respects that a lady owes someone like you!"

The youth got up[Sp)] and went back 'to the lady's house.[Sp)] He was ordered to clean himself up. Then he remained with her for that day, idling and at leisure.[2]

When it came evening, she granted him five hundred dirhems, and off he went to his companions, and wrote on the city wall:

❧ Beauty is Worth Five Hundred Dirhems in One Day!! ❧

[C. The Merchant's Son]

When they arose in the morning, they said to the merchant's son: "Earn us something with your intelligence and merchandizing!"

So he went off and only a little while passed before he noticed a great ship at sea which was anchoring off shore not far from the city. People were going out to buy what was in it, for its owners were already bargaining.

Then they said: "Let's go away today until we can beat them down, and they will charge us less."

So they did that.

The merchant's son stayed on afterwards, and bought up what was in it from them for one hundred thousand dirhems. When the merchants learned of it, they came to him and gave him a profit of another hundred thousand. He took the cash, turned his purchase over to them, and returned to his companions.

As he was passing by the city gate, he wrote on it:

INTELLIGENCE HAS THE
VALUE OF 100,000
DIRHEMS A DAY. $ $ $

So they enjoyed what they had received, and felt they had plenty.

[D. The King's Son]

When they arose on the fourth morning,[3] they said to the king's son: "Go off and earn something for us with fate and luck!"

So he went off till he came to the city gate, and he sat down on one of the benches by it.

Now it occurred that the king had passed away leaving no son, brother, or kinsman. They passed by him with the king's bier, and noticed how he did not get excited, frightened, nor saddened at the king's death.

So one of the men asked him: "Who are you, and why have you sat down at the city gate? Doesn't the king's death sadden you?"

He did not answer him, so he insulted him and drove him away. As soon as they had passed, he returned to his spot; so when they were coming back, the one who had acted in that manner saw him and said:

"Didn't I forbid you this seat?"

He walked right up to him, and seized and jailed him.

'Next day$^{Y/CeD)}$ when they gathered to appoint some man as king over themselves, they chose the one who had ordered [the lad] thrown in jail. He told his story, saying:

"'I want to say what happened yesterday: when we were bearing the king's body, I saw a youth sitting on a bench^{Sp} by the city gate$^{Y/CeD}$. He seemed a strange man from his manner and dress, and^{Sp} I saw he was not sad like us, as if the affair did not matter to him; while he had an air of majesty and nobility^Y. I spoke to him and he did not answer me$^{Y/CeD}$, so I drove him away from the gate^Y. As we were returning, I saw him sitting$^{Y/CeD}$ in that spot, and^{Sp} taking him for a spy, I had him seized and put in jail$^{Y/CeD)}$.'"

So they sent for him. He was brought, and they asked him who he was, what his business was, and what had brought him to their land.

He said: "I am a son of the king of Qarunad. My father passed away, and my brother deprived me of the kingdom, although I am older than he; so I fled from him in fear of my life, until I reached you."

When they heard that from him, and had understood his language, (for one of them who had traveled in his country knew it), they bowed down to him, appointed him their king,[4] and invested him with their administration.

It was their custom to hold a parade whenever they made anyone their king; so they mounted him on an elephant and went the rounds. When they were passing by the city gate, he noticed what his companions had written as he was looking at it; so he ordered the following to be inscribed:[5]

> TOIL, INTELLIGENCE, AND BEAUTY,
> AND WHATEVER BEFALLS MAN OF GOOD OR EVIL
> IS THROUGH DESTINY AND FATE.
> CONSIDER THEREFORE HOW GOD HAS FAVORED ME
> WITH GOODNESS AND HAPPINESS THROUGH
> HIS GRACE!

Then the king came into his council, and he sat upon his throne and sent for his companions. They came to him, and he granted them riches and made them wealthy. 'The man of understanding he made one of his ministers; he established the industrious son of the husbandman amongst the cultivators of the soil; and having ordered a large sum of money to be given to the handsome man, he sent him away, that he might not corrupt the morals of the ladies of his court[Kn)].

Then he gathered his officers and the prominent people and persons of insight from the inhabitants of his kingdom, and he said: "My companions are convinced that God has bestowed good on them only through destiny and fate, and that He is responsible for what they have. As for myself, what God has granted and bestowed upon me, has not been for beauty nor intelligence nor toil.

"When my brother drove me away and terrorized me, I did not hope to attain to this dignity nor to be here, for I have seen finer and handsomer people than myself amongst the people of this land, and I know that there are persons who are more perfect than I in judgment and harder workers. God and destiny drove me to emigrate, so that the matter was fulfilled; God indeed labored and decreed, for I was already resigned to existing in a state of hardship and making a difficult living."

Then a pilgrim who was in that land rose up and said: "Your majesty, you have indeed spoken with patience, intelligence, and judgment. Our opinion and our hopes in you are fine, and we realize what you are telling and we believe what you describe. We know that when God drove you from your home, you were worthy of the excellence which He has granted you, and may His blessings continue upon you!

"For the happiest man in this world and the next, and the most joyful, is he upon whom God has bestowed the like of what He has bestowed upon you, and done the like as He has done with you. We see indeed that we were loving God when we made you king over us and invested you with our administration; so we praise God that He has been so generous towards us and has thereby favored us."

Then another pilgrim stood up and praised God, thanking and glorifying Him and enumerating His bounties. He said:

[D1. The Grateful Pigeons]

"Your majesty, when I was a lad, before I became a pilgrim, I served a certain 'noble^η' man. When it seemed that I ought to renounce the world, I left him and he gave me two dirhems as my wages.

"I wanted to offer alms with one of them, and to spend the other, so I said: 'There is nothing more important for the next world than buying a soul for a dirhem and freeing it to the glory of God.'

"So I went to the market and found two pigeons with a fowler. I bargained with him for them both, but he refused to come down from two dirhems for the pair of them. I strove to have him give them both to me for one dirhem, but he refused to.

"So I said: 'Perhaps they are mates or brothers, and I fear that the other will die if I free only one of them.'

"So I bought them both from him for the price which he named. I was anxious lest if I set them loose in inhabited country, they would not be able to fly from being so weak from what they had suffered in the way of exhaustion, 'and I was not sure but they would be caught again^{Y/CeD)}. So I went off with them to a place where there was much pasturage, and I freed them. They both flew away and lighted upon a tree; then I started to return.

"One of them said to the other: 'This hermit has freed us from the straits we were in, and we should reward him for his action.'

"Then they said to me: 'We ought to thank you for what you have brought us, and acknowledge it. We thus acknowledge it to you: at the foot of this tree there is a jar full of dirhems; so take it.'[6]

"I went to the tree, doubting what they had said to me. Yet I only dug a little till I came to 'the jar^$\mathfrak{P}$' and pulled it out.

"I called upon God for their health,[7] and said to them both: 'Since this shows that you know what is underground, and you fly between heaven and earth, then how is it that you fell into this plight from which I rescued you?'

"They said: 'Don't you know, you clever man, that when fate befalls one, it injures his vision? Fate overcomes everything, and one is unable to get beyond it nor to hem it in.'

Then the philosopher said to the king: "People should know how to look into matters and understand them, for all things are according to destiny and fate. No one can win it for himself just by wanting it, nor avert it through loathing it, for everything belongs to God, who does as He pleases and decides as He chooses. Thus our souls are tranquil and trust in Him, since whomsoever God inspires and fashions, has happiness and peace."

Here Ends the Chapter of
the King and his
Companions.

Chapter XIII

The Chapter

of the Archer and the Lioness

[or Why People Reform][1]

HE KING said to the philosopher: "I have heard what you mentioned about destiny and fate, and how they both overcome matters. Now inform me about one who stops hurting others because of what he suffered in the way of harm and what he has received as a warning and reproach for showing injury and enmity towards others."

The philosopher said: "One does not 'venture to$^{Y/CeD)}$ seek what will harm people and wrong them, but only ignorant and foolish people with a bad view of consequences in this world and the other, and with little knowledge of what they will thereby incur as a stroke of punishment and will befall them as a result of what they acquire without understanding the word 'intelligence^{n}.

"If one of them should be saved from some impiety which occurred before the mischief they committed can befall them, the next world will overtake them, for which words and the powers of description fall short of its awful seriousness and importance.

"Often the ignorant man is warned and ponders what 'disgusting things^{n} will strike him, so that he refrains from injuring or hating anyone, and as a consequence his abstention is worth his while. Corresponding to that tale is the story of the archer, the lioness, the jackal, 'and the turtledove^{n}."

The king said: "What was that?"

Bidpai the philosopher said:

184

ONCE UPON A TIME a lioness lived in a thicket 'by the seashore⁽⁾'. She had two cubs, and she used to go out to seek game and leave them both alone. A hunter passed by and ran across them. He killed and stripped them of their pelts, and carried them off home.

When she returned and found what had become of them, an abominable, dreadful, and heart-rending business, her eyes burned and her grief and rage were great. She was upset for a long time, and she beat her back and her belly and shrieked.

Now she had a jackal as next-door neighbor. When he heard those shrieks and outbursts she was making, he said:

"What ever has happened to make you shout so? Come and tell me about it, so I can sympathize with you and offer you some consolation."

So the lioness said: "My cubs! An archer passed by and killed them! He stripped them of their pelts, picked them up, and threw them away naked!"

The jackal said: "Don't carry on so! Stop shouting and purify yourself. You know that this archer has only done to you what you have constantly done to others. Rage and grief will not help you get your cubs back, seeing that you have done so to his loved ones, and have treated him the same and even worse.

"Endure the same from another as he has borne from you, for it has been said: Thou shalt be treated as thou hast treated;² and the fruit of action is punishment and reward, and they are both in proportion to their greatness or smallness. It is just as when reapers appear, the planter gives each according to his calculation of how much seed they sowed."

The lioness said: "Show me that more clearly, and explain it to me."

The jackal said: "How old are you?"

The lioness said: "One hundred years."

He said: "What do you live off and eat?"

The lioness said: "The meat of wild animals."

The jackal said: "Have these wild animals fathers and mothers?"

The lioness said: "Of course."

So the jackal said: "Why then don't we hear these fathers and mothers making the same racket, and groaning and crying like we see you doing? That only happened because you look at consequences wrongly and fail to consider them. You were ignorant of how harm would return to you."

When the lioness heard ⟨what the jackal told her$^{Y/CeD)}$, she realized that she had earned that and brought it down upon herself. She was muddled and perplexed, for whoever acts unjustly and unrighteously is punished and overcome. So she gave up game and started eating fruit instead of meat, taking up asceticism and piety.

Then ⟨a turtledove who owned that bush and$^{\eta}$ made his living from its fruits saw that she was eating many of them, and he said to her:

"I had thought there was little fruit from the amount that is missing, and that the trees had not borne this year; but when I see you eating it while you are carnivorous, and how you have renounced what God has set aside for you, and changed over to a different type of subsistence from your own, to use it up when it isn't yours, I know that while the trees have borne fruit as they have borne it in times past, scarcity like this has only come on your account.

So woe to the trees and the fruits! And to whoever lives off them! Their doom and ruination is at hand, when he who has no right nor share in it contends for them."

⟨When the lioness heard what the turtledove had to say$^{\eta}$, she left off eating fruits and started eating grass and practicing piety.

"I have only made this fable up for you so that ⟨you may know$^{Y/CeD)}$ that the ignorant man often leaves off ugly action merely from the harm which people deal him, like the lioness who stopped eating the flesh of wild animals because of what had happened to her cubs, and then because of the ⟨turtledove's$^{\eta}$ speech, she ate grass and took up asceticism and piety."

Then the philosopher said to the king: "People are right in looking upon that with approval and accepting whatever falls their lot, for indeed it has been said: Do unto others as you would be done by. There is only justice in that, and in justice lies the way to please both God and man."

Here Ends the Chapter of the Archer,
the Lioness, and the Jackal.

Chapter XIV

The Chapter

of the Hermit and his Guest

[or Be Content with your Lot]¹

HE KING said to the philosopher: "I have heard what you mentioned about the man who harms another and ʿstops doing soᵍᵖ⁾ because of the damage which has befallen him or the misfortune which occurs to him. Now inform me, if you think it fitting, about one who stops doing the work which suits and corresponds to him, and who seeks something else not within his reach; and so he returns to what he had before and cannot do that either. Thus he will remain perplexed and confused."

The philosopher said:

ONCE UPON A TIME in the land of Karkh there lived an earnest hermit. One day a guest dropped in on him and asked for some fruit to be brought him. [He offered him] ʿdatesʸ/ᶜᵉᴰ and butter, which are strange things in that landˢᵖ⁾; so they ate them together.

Then the guest said: "How sweet are these ʿdatesʸ/ᶜᵉᴰ and how good! In the country where I live, there are no palms. Even so, there are some fruits which are satisfying, although they cannot measure up to ʿdatesˢᵖ⁾ nor equal them as sweet fruit. Still they are satisfying and nourishing, considering the indigestibility of dates and their unsuitablilty for the body."

So the hermit said: "One is considered unfortunate if he cannot do without what isn't available. He becomes greedy and impatient, and the bother of it becomes a burden and a hardship that injures and overwhelms him. You ʿhave a happy fate if you are content with what you find, and abstain from what you do not findⁿ."

The guest said: "You are correct and on the right track!"

ʿNow this hermit knew Hebrew, and the guest once heard him speaking it. He found the language pleasing, and he admired itⁿ.

[So the guest remarked]: "I have heard you uttering strange words which fascinate me, they seem so beautiful. If you will teach them to me, I will be eager and anxious to learn them."

'He undertook to learn them, and bent himself to that for some days[n].

Then the hermit said: "If you give up your own language and take up the Hebrew tongue, the same will befall you as happened to the crow."

The guest said: "What was that?"

The hermit said:

[A. The Crow Who Would Walk Like a Partridge]

"Once upon a time a crow saw a partridge walking, and he was intrigued with its gait and yearned to learn it. He took lessons, and was unable to master it.

"So he went back to his previous way of walking, but he had forgotten that, and he bacame perplexed and confused. Thus he attained neither what he had sought nor yet did he perform well what he once possessed.

"Now I have made this fable up to teach you that if you abandon your own language and take pains to acquire the Hebrew speech which does not belong to you, you will not attain it and will forget the other which you had. For it has been said: He is reckoned ignorant who tried to control matters which do not suit him nor belong to his family, and which his fathers and ancestors before him neither attained nor knew."

The philosopher said to the king: "Nowadays rulers in their slight concern for their subjects' welfare are wrong in letting people change their social status, so that they disregard their duty and adopt a way of living which is dangerous to kings.[2]

"When people of the lower classes seek to climb to a higher class and long to handle administration, they ruin good breeding and provoke dissension between the baseborn and the nobles. Then things reach such a stage that it incurs great and serious damage, and there is opposition to the king within his own kingdom."

Here Ends the Chapter of the Hermit and his Guest.

Chapter XV

The Chapter

of the Pigeon, the Fox, and the Crane

[or Don't Get Fooled by your own Trick][1]

(It being a chapter about someone who sees another's point of view, but fails to see his own.)

THE KING said to the philosopher: "I have heard this fable indeed, so make me up a story about the man who sees someone else's point of view, but not his own."

The philosopher said: "That story is the fable about the pigeon, the fox, and the crane."

The king said: "What is that fable?"

The philosopher said:

ONCE UPON A TIME a pigeon had hatched her young on the top of a tall palm tree which soared up to heaven. When the pigeon had started to build the nest on the top of that palm, she managed it only after hardship and toil and difficulty, because of its height and tallness. When she finished building it, she laid her eggs there and then hatched them.

The chicks had pecked their eggs open and were growing up, when the fox came to her. He used to do this whenever he knew that her fledglings were learning to fly. He would stand at the foot of the palm and shout to her, threatening to climb up if she did not throw her chicks down to him.[2]

One day while her chicks were growing up, a crane approached and lighted upon the palm. When he saw the pigeon was distressed and sad and extremely worried, he said to her:

"O pigeon, why do I see you with your mind upset and in such a bad humor?"

So she said to him: "O crane, a fox has always outwitted me every time my chicks have grown up. He comes and threatens me, shouting from the foot of the palm. So I am frightened and fling him my chicks."

The crane said to her: "When he comes to do what you mention, tell him: 'I won't throw you my chicks! Climb up and help yourself! If you do that and eat my chicks, I shall still fly away from you and save myself.' "

When the crane had taught her that trick, he flew away and alighted on the bank of a river.

So the fox approached at the time he knew, and stood underneath her. Then he shouted as was his custom.

The pigeon answered as the heron had taught her.

The fox said to her: "Tell me who taught you this?"

She said: "The crane taught me."

So the fox went off till he came to the crane on the riverbank, and found him standing there.

The fox said to him: "O crane, when the wind comes from your right, where do you place your head?"

He said: "To my left."

He said: "When it comes to you on your left, where do you put your head?"

He said: "I place it to my right or behind me."[3]

'The fox[SP]' said: "When the wind comes to you from all sides and every direction, where do you put it?"

'The crane[SP]' said: "I place it under my wing."

He said: "And how do you put it under your wing? I don't see how it is possible for you!"

He said: "Of course it is."

'The fox[SP]' said: "Show me how you do it, for upon my life, O nations of birds, God has preferred you over us! You know in one hour the same as we know in a year, and you accomplish what we can never accomplish. You place your heads under your wings because of the cold and the wind, and it is all to your favor. Show me how you do it!"

So the bird put his head under his wing. The fox sprang upon him from where he was standing and seized him, biting him so as to break his neck. Then he said to him:

"O enemy of yourself! You saw the pigeon's point of view, and taught her a trick to save herself; but you were unable to do so for yourself. Thus your enemy has overpowered you."

Then he killed and ate him.

Thus Ends the Chapter of the
Pigeon, the Fox, and
the Crane.

GOD BE EVER PRAISED:
THE BOOK IS ENDED.

NOTES

INTRODUCTION

1 *KF*, pp. lvi ff. and p. lxxxvi.

CHAPTER I

1 There is some divergence in the versions concerning the characters of Kalilah and Dimnah; but the narrative confirms that Dimnah was the worse.

2 باب 'gate' in Arabic is translated literally in Spanish, instead of by *corte*. Later on, *ala puerta del rrey* ('at the king's gate') is *CeD's* باب السلطان ('at the sultan's gate, court'). This usage accounts for the expression 'The Sublime Porte' in reference to the Ottoman court.

Cf. also notes II.5 and XI. 4, as well as other places not indicated.

3 This reads 'testicles', but I have changed it for obvious purposes. Knatchbull uses the same colloquial euphemism.

4 Note Dimnah's neat psychological trick of sharing the fright, which *CeD* misses.

5 All this verbiage seems redundant, but it is more or less confirmed by *Eg*. p. 295. Anyhow, it is just how anyone mulls over such problems mentally.

6 *Ay* p. 83, n. 5** suggests that this is a corruption of the second part of مدينة الدائن . I agree, but still include it in order to give one more personal name to the story. Besides, it might also be a corruption of the Mahilāropya from which so many characters in *P* come (Cf. note III.6).

7 In *Ch* this is the man's anus, and the sneeze corresponds to his breaking wind. I have preferred the *CeD* rendering since is is less vulgar and equally plausible. The same alteration is made in the new Persian version.

8 *Eg* "When a wise man is attackt and sees no escape for himself, then he dies fighting along with his foe."

9 *Ch* groups the first two in a common dual حازمان ; *Y* has the simple form حازم plus the superlative احزم right from the start; and *CeD* uses *enviso* and *delibre*. which are both totally different roots. I am following the Spanish method.

193

¹⁰ *Ch* p. 43, n., calls this passage *très alambiqué*, which alas is only too true. *KF* helps somewhat in straightening it up.

¹¹ This is one of the prototypes of the 'Dog and his Shadow' story. A better one occurs in Burzōē's Introduction (*An* II.253-56.).

¹² This occurs in La Fontaine as *Les Animaux malades de la peste*. Notice also how both the camel in this story and Shatrabah himself were left behind by merchants; and how the lion falls ill as in the story of the Donkey without Ears or Heart (*V.A.*).

¹³ This reminds one of the story of Lot and Sodom.

¹⁴ *KwD* is subtler here, for the crow lets on that the lion acquiesced; whereas in *CeD* he is rather a fellow plotter. However, I have left the lion in the crow's first statement immediately following to be consistent with the thread of the story.

¹⁵ The sandpipers in *Eg* and 'strandbirds' (*ṭiṭṭibha*, which reaches Spanish almost intact as *tittuy*); in *DVH* as *avis aquatica*; and in *KF* by 'sandpiper'. I am translating this as in *KF*, and not 'seagull' like Pérez, pp. 5 and 40.

In *P* the story is much clearer, and it is better to read it there. I am adding enough to make the narrative fairly understandable, as for instance, stating clearly that the 'Griffin Eagle' is Garuḍa, the mythical bird ridden by Viṣṇu, and of Indonesian Airlines.

¹⁶ In La Fontaine, this occurs as *La Tortue et les deux canards*.

¹⁷ Cf. *Eg* p. 317: "Fourfold political methods are known, beginning with conciliation, and ending with violence. But of these violence is the worst; therefore it should be avoided. Conciliation, bribery, and sowing of dissention, these three are an ever-open door of wisdom. But the fourth method is declared by the noble to be heroic action."

¹⁸ i.e., he always can find all he wants of them; cf. *Eg* p. 319.

¹⁹ Both *P* and *CeD* have 'heron', which would seem better than *KwD*'s 'drake', which I am changing to 'duck'. Cf. the Heron and the Crayfish, story I.E1; and the Pigeon, the Fox and the Crane, XV. The weasel is also really a mongoose in *P*, as in the Hermit and the Mongoose, story VI.

²⁰ *Eg* p. 325: "An honest wise man should be cultivated; with a crafty wise man one should be on his guard; an honest fool, however, is to be trusted with compassion; while a crafty fool should be shunned utterly."

²¹ In both *P* and *CeD*, Dimnah gets still higher rank; but evidently neither *Ch*, *Y*, nor *KF* appreciated such an honor. That is why I have enclosed it in parentheses. This gloss is of course confirmed by the next chapter, which is pure interpolation from the Pahlavi version.

CHAPTER II

[1] Cf.*Ch* p. 49, n.; Benfey I, 297-99; a,d *KF* p. 387, n. This story is not in *P*, but was added in the Pahlavi, as witness the parrot talking in Bactrian, story II.D. This might be adduced as showing Persian background.

[2] Compare the position of the other dowager in story X.

[3] *CeD* and *Y* have the lion lower his head as a sign of mourning for Shatrabah.

[4] شَنَّى , شَبَّى , or even سَنَّى might be read here. Cf. *Ay* p. 175, n. 1[a].

[5] *CeD* has *puerta* for باب , as in note I.2.

[6] I am eliminating "your true friend and adviser, the leopard," because it is non consistent with the revelation later on p.70, nor with the thread of the narrative.

[7] *Ch* p. 52 suggests the change of انابل to انابل , which is confirmed by *CeD's non diga*.

[8] Ch صاحب ـ مائد ة اللزى ; *CeD: 'cozinero mayor'; KF* 'butler'; *Y* سيد الخبازبر 'master of the pigs'. This latter certainly demonstrates that the origin of this fable was not Islamic.

[9] Could this have been the Christian Mote and Beam influence?

[10] Cf. *Y's* name for the jackal immediately above. Only one additional diacritical point in Arabic renders them identical.

[11] The title would indicate a Persian origin for this story at least. The Bactrian visitors might also be so interpreted. Spanish garbles into as transliteration *Morzuben*, and thus misses the connotation of satrap.

CHAPTER III

[1] Cf. W. N. Brown, "A Comparative Translation of the Arabic *Kalilah wa-Dimnah*, Chapter VI," in *JAOS* 42:215-250 (Chapter VI is one of the many numberings); and *Putnam's Magazine*, July 1868, pp. 76-81. This chapter is generally called 'The Ringdove', although the pigeon's post is only introductory.

[2] الخور , البر , or ابى for الخير ؟ *Y* has الجر and *CeD lugar de muchos árboles.*

[3] العمران ; *CeD poblado; Eg.* 'rugged country'; *KF* "As long as we fly over the open country, the fowler will not despair of us, but will keep running after us. But let us fly among the houses, so that the way may appear intricate to him, and he may despair of us and turn back in shame and disappointment."

[4] Cf. *Eg*, which is much more detailed here (II.333-34); and *Ch's* MS *B*.

[5] *Ch* كذه 'hand'; *Y* and *Ch's* MS *B* كـ ; *CeD seno; Eg* 'bosom'. *Sp* and *P* confirm each other.

⁶ In *P* this is Mahilāropya, the same place as Shatrabah comes from in Chapter I, and near where the crow's tree is in this. Almost any city beginning with M seems to be a misspelling of Mahilāropya (see note I.6). Similarly *CeD* seems desirous to make all countries as close to the name 'Georgia' as possible.

⁷ *Ch* جعل يأكل مسه ; *CeD meóse en*; *Y* نعاد فيه ; *P* has it defiled by the dog's touch rather than his urine.

⁸ Since the wadi is calle a coulee in western North America, I am using this word. Notice how *CeD* missed this figure, using *río* for both types of streams.

⁹ This thought is all essentially Hindu, that one must withdraw from the world and not work or toil. Even beggary or theft seem to be preferable. The argumentation is much clearer in *Eg*. Note, however, how surprisingly modern is the psychology of the next paragraph.

CHAPTER IV

¹ *Eg* "Just as in the case of sticks, a man's shadow is lenghthened when he bends, and yet if he bends too much, it is completely destroyed; hence one should bend, but not overmuch."

² Cf. *Ay* p. 262, n. 5, about the part that is missing. Both *CeD* and *P* help clear up *KwD*. *Eg* combines the minister and the messenger, while I prefer to separate it as in *CeD*, and to drop out his ablutions.

³ *Eg* "He who apportions his income and outlay, whose agents are secret and whose counsel is private, and who speaks not unkindly to his ministers—he shall rule the earth to the edge of the ocean."

⁴ Notice how   'opening' and therefore by extension in meaning 'victory', is translated *espacio* or 'space' in *CeD*. A medieval application of *Lebensraum*.

⁵ This is رب, and not الله 'God'. This fable gets more and more pagan as it goes along, although *CeD* has *Dios*. The Spanish is especially pagan.

⁶ *Cg* على ظلم أحدٌ بيضر ; *Y* دلم يطلح ; ; *CeD Pocos son los que vençen que non se engreyan*; and *Eg* "Who is not made insolent by good fortune?"

⁷ *Ch* questions the reading المربض ; but *Sp cobdiçioso* confirms it.

⁸ In *CeD* and *Y* there is no change of speaker until "I pray God . . . "

⁹ Substituting الحدأ 'kite' for *Y*'s الجدأ 'kid'. Cf. also *CeD*'s mistaken *milano* (also 'kite'), which shows that the error must be quite ancient. Cf. *Eg* p. 390, v. 114; and *Ay* p. 302, note 6*. *CeD* is deficient in other ways too, in this passage.

¹⁰ Notice how *Ch* corrects *CeD*'s *del omne dioso* to *odioso*. Pérez, p. 10, still reads this as the equivalent of *añoso*.

CHAPTER V

¹ P: 'crocodile'.

² P: 'women'.

³ الكّاسب P: 'actors on the stage'. KwD says that he plays on a piece of wood, which might be the 'boards'; but I am taking it for the minstrels who come around to play for parties at home.

⁴ This does not occur in CeD. Observe also Ch's note, and Eg: p. 272, n. 4. This is the famous Hindu 'Group of Three' which is needed for a full living: 1) religion, 2) politics, and 3) love.

⁵ CeD says that the lion would take this as an omen: por agüero.

CHAPTER VI

¹ CeD's MS A has this mongoose a dog can; MS B has it a cat gato; while Ch has it ابن عرس or 'weasel'. However, in P it is a mongoose, and I have reverted to this name since it is evidently a domestic animal which hunts snakes. This is the same mistake as in the story of the Smart Duck (I.M1), where a P mongoose changes form in migrating from India to Spain.

² Cf. La Fontaine's fable La Laitière et le pot au lait, the story of Truhana in El Conde Lucanor, and the Arabian Nights story of Jilad and Shammās, all of which have this for a prototype. Miller discusses it in Chips, IV:154, ff.

³ With this story we also come to the end of that portion of Kalilah and Dimnah which is derived from P. The next chapters have all been added to KwD either in the Pahlavi or in the Arabic. The order varies according to the different versions of KwD and CeD; but I am holding to Ch's order rather than confusing the issue further.

CHAPTER VII

¹ This is Chapter IX in Ch. XI in CeD and XIII in Y. Guidi should be consulted about the order of the chapters.

In CeD the three main characters are called: Beled, Cederano and Elbes, respectively. I am not attempting to explain these or any other variants after KF's excellent work in that line; but only to keep the characters distinct in the narrative, following Ch's nomenclature.

This story is very anticlerical, and as might be expected, CeD missed the point entirely, as evidenced by the various mistranscriptions of the word 'Brahaman', which seems to mystify the Spanish translators.

Through all of this, KF is very helpful, since P does not contain the story, and the parries are quite intricate between Ayādh and Shādaram. However, it is still amazing that all versions are as close as they are.

² CeD completely misses the point here, much as it is otherwise interested in religious matters and characters. Witness the Spanish renderings of 'Brahmans': Albarhamium, Albarhamiud, Alvarhamin, etc.; these are all plays upon the Arabic البرهمون. However, Observe the next note also.

³ *CeD* here does say that the Brahmans complain that the king *ha muerto nuestros sacerdotes*, but evidently does not couple the Brahamans with the idea that they are a priestly order.

⁴ On p. 308, *KF* gives an excellent list of some of these kings and their kingdoms; but they are so mixed up here that I am merely sticking to *Ch* in the first instance, and to *CeD* and *Y* in the second and third.

⁵ *CeD* has an intersting aside here: *ca los rreyes de India solían comer mucho arroz*, as if rice might still not be a staple of Spanish diet at the time—or perhaps not in Toledo.

⁶ Note how Ayādh's ethics go only so far as to save the queen without crossing the king.

⁷ *CeD* makes this into four by separating the criminal from the crime in this fashion: (1) *el mal fechor et* (2) *el que juistiçia al que [non] faze por qué.*

⁸ This question and its answer are not in *CeD*.

⁹ This statement and response are not in *CeD*, but they are confirmed by *KF*.

¹⁰ This is how I translate المملوك 'al-mamlūk' or 'slave of white race', which Spanish renders *vasallo*, following its feudal mentality. Later on العبد or 'black slave' is rendered *siervo*; while سيده 'his master, lord' is also rendered *señor* in *CeD* rather than *amo*.

¹¹ *CeD* adds a fourth: *Et el que dize delo que es ya fecho e passado:* «*Quisiese Dios que non fuesse*». The next four parries are not in *CeD* at all.

¹² These last two examples do not appear in *CeD*, nor does the next parry.

¹³ The next seven parries are not in *CeD*.

¹⁴ Dropping the point in الحبيد to read الحديد, so as to conform with *KF* p. 240, 11.22-23.

¹⁵ *KF* has 'sweet and bitter' instead. *CeD* has a parry here which does not occur until the next page in *Ch*; i.e., the fifth next, which is the same place as it occurs in *KF* also. The next three parries are not in *CeD* either.

¹⁶ *CeD* has a parry which comes a page later in *Ch*. The next three parries are missing in *CeD*.

¹⁷ Cf. صاحب السبع and *et al que cria los árboles* (الشجر vs. السبع) *et cobdiçia toda vía que crescan por tal de aver ende algo.* Both *KF* and common sense confirm *Ch*.

¹⁸ The next two paragraphs are not in *CeD*.

¹⁹ This last means that in murdering, he himself gets killed.

²⁰ *Kf* "nakedness which puts to shame."

²¹ *KF* "a husbandman in tilling his land"; *CeD Et el savidor en obrar.* The Spanish is rather loose; *Sy* more precise; while if we change the points in

KwD from والعالم بالحرب ← اعمال الحرب, to read الحرب اعمال ← بالحرب والعالم, we thereby get "the master plowman in how he plows," which I prefer.

CHAPTER VIII

[1] This is Chapter IX in CeD, following the 'Hermit and the Mongoose', where is also occurs in KF and Y. The first sentence in Ch might tend to prove the misplacement.

CHAPTER IX

[1] This story is from the Mahabharata XII (cf. KF p. 296; and Ch pp. 63-64, n). Note also that Fanzah is always masculine in KwD and feminine in CeD.

[2] From the beginning of this speech down to here, MS C of Ch has been followed.

[3] I prefer this to the KwD 'dogs', although the Hindu content would be more averse to eating bovines than canines, whereas the reverse would be true in Islam and Christianity.

CHAPTER X

[1] This is Chapter XIV in Ced; but in KF, King Shadaram occurs at the very end of the book, and thus this is after the same chapter as in KwD actually.

[2] Cf. KF p. xlviii, where he says this was because in another life the jackal had been an evil king.

[3] Compare this dowager and the one in the story of Dimnah's Trial (Chapter II). This is one character which has not been altered in the slightest in passing from India to Spain, although the circumstances are similar in this role in any country where there is royalty.

CHAPTER XI

[1] Guidi says this is a Buddhist fable. It is certainly a curious mixture of gratitude rewarded, and of witless evil. The basic theme is quite ethical, but the mechanics of the narrative require an immoral element like the murder of the princess, in order to keep it moving.

[2] CeD has the tiger a *tejón* or badger, which necessitates some alteration in the plot, as shown in the next note.

[3] In the Spanish version, the monkey connives with the badger—which as we have noted has replaced the tiger in CeD—to steal the jewels, since the badger was not as nimble as the KwD prototype.

[4] باب 'gate' once more (cf. note I.2). In this instance, CeD translates this as *alcáçar*, which is another word borrowed directly from the Arabic القصر , although it in turn has a Latin origin, *castrum*.

5 I have interchanged a good deal in the next three or four paragraphs, in order to help the continuity of the narrative.

6 The charm and the antidote are not in *CeD*, because in that version the pilgrim uses his powers of prayer exclusively.

CHAPTER XII

1 Could this be called bourgeois rationalism? This whole discussion is much longer in *CeD*.

2 This story is much longer in *CeD*, and as *KwD* is too concise, I have included enough of the *Sp* to help the story along, but not enough to distort it. In one place, the maid says that her mistress is *Doña Fulana, muger de don Fulano*, which might conceivably indicate an Arabic prototype for the expansion; and later on she has all the companions come and live off her bounty for several days, which I think is pure editorial expansion. It is therefore omitted for the same reasons as the part mentioned in the next note.

3 *CeD* says: *después de ende a días*, as if they lived off their earnings for a while. However, *Ch*, *Y*, and *KF* all agree that now they wanted to try their luck the very next day.

4 *CeD* makes the king, who has already been appointed, the prince's friend, and the latter then protects him.

5 This is much more extensive in *CeD*, and has the alterations of the prince making friends with the new king of the city, who equips him to lead an army to recover his own throne. Also, none of the companions has written anything on the city gate before, so he makes up for their oversight by a long-winded all-inclusive statement.

Ay p. 448, n. 2, gives up trying to collate *CeD* and *KwD* at this point, although an underlying textual unity can be sensed. Thus my own feeling that the *Sp* changes are purely editorial.

6 Here the pigeons tell the pilgrim to dig by the tree; in *CeD* they lead him on to it and go through the motions of digging.

7 *CeD* here asks God to grant them speech so he can talk with them, their first words in *Sp*. This alternation is the same as observed above in note XI.6, and thus these also must be editorial.

CHAPTER XIII

1 This chapter occurs between the jackal-monk and the lion-king in *Y*; and as Chapter XIII in *CeD*; but it follows the preceding 'Four Companions' in *KF* as in *Ch*. *KF* says on p. 300 that it seems to be a Hindu fable, but that it cannot be traced in Indian literature. On the other hand, the emphasis on the Golden Rule and on eschatology would tend to make it of a Christian origin. In *CeD* this occurs in MS *B* only.

² This may be a Christian element. Cf. Matthew VII:2: "For with what judgment ye judge, ye shall be judged; and with what measure ye mete, it shall be measured unto you."

CHAPTER XIV

¹ This, because of the mention of dates and of Hebrew, is thought not to be Hindu either. Cf. *KF* p. 301 n.; *An* p. x; and Benfey. *Ch* points out how the kernel fable is Arabian in origin. It is certainly a story to make people desirous of maintaining the social status quo. In *CeD* it also is found only in MS *B*.

² Could this be medieval feudal or modern 'corporatist' theory?

CHAPTER XV

¹ Cf. *Ch* p. 63 and p. ٢٤٧ ;and *An* p. x. This is not in *Ch*'s original, but occurs last in both *CeD* and *Y*, and is therefore appended here. I am omitting the 'King of the Rats and his Ministers' because that is only an appendix in *Ch* and does not occur at all in *CeD*; and the 'Cranes and the Duck' which occurs in *Sp* only and in neither of our *KwD* texts. Cf. *Ay* p. 457, n. 1; and *Ch* p. 67, n.

² Compare this and the other story of the 'Snake and the Duck' (story I.M1).

³ All this is very much longer in *CeD*.

BIBLIOGRAPHY

Alemany y Bolufer, José. *La antigua versión de Calila y Dimna*. Madrid: 1915.

Allen, Clifford G. *L'ancienne version espagnole de Kalila et Digna*. Macon: 1906.

Amin Ma'luf (Malouf). *An Arabic Zoological Dictionary*. Cairo: 1932.

Andres, Giovanni. *Dell'origine, progressi e stato attuale d'ogni Litteratura*, 7 vols. Parma: 1782-98.

Arnold, Sir Thomas, and Guillaume, Alfred. *The Legacy of Islam*. Oxford: 1931.

'Azzam, 'A. *Kitab Kalila wa-Dimna*, ed. Dr. Tahrin Bek and Dr. Abd al-Wahab. Cairo, 1941.

Bédier, Joseph. *Les Fabliaux*, 4th. ed. Paris: 1925.

Benfey, Theodor. *Pantschatantra*. Leipzig: 1859.

——————————. *Die Alte spanische Übersetzung des Kalila und Dimnah (Orient und Occident)*.Gottingen: 1862.

Bickell, Gustav. *Kalilag und Damnag*. Leipzig: 1876. (Introduction by Th. Benfey).

Brockelmann, Karl. *Geschichte der arabische Litteratur*, 2 vols. Weimar: 1898-1902.

Brown, W. N. "A Comparative Translation of the Arabic Kalilah wa-Dimnah, Chapter VI." *JAOS* XLII:215-250.

Castro, Américo. "Vocabulario latino-español de la Edad Media." *RFE* 1936.

Cejador y Frauca, Julio. *Vocabulario medieval castellano*. Madrid: 1929.

Chandler, Frank W. *The Literature of Roguery*, 2 vols. Boston: 1907.

Cheikho, Louis. *La version arabe de Kalilah et Dimnah*, 2nd. ed. Beirut: 1923. (1st. ed., Beirut: 1905).

Cosquin, E. C. *Contes populaires de Lorraine*, 2 vols. Paris: 1862.

Clouston, Wm. A. *Popular Tales and fictions*, 2 vols. Edinburgh: 1887.

Cuervo, Rufino José. *Diccionario de construcción y régimen*, 2 vols. Paris: 1888-93.

Davids, T. W. Rhys. *Buddhist birth stories or Jataka tales*. London: 1880.

Delisle, Léopold. "Notice sur les fables latines d'origine indienne." *Journal des Savants* 1898.

Derenbourg, Joseph. *Deux versions hébraiques du livre de Kalilah et Dimnah*. Paris: 1881.

——————————. *Johannis de Capua Directorium vitae humanae.* Paris, 1887.

Dietrich, Günther. *Syntaktisches zur Kalilah wa-Dimnah.* Kirchhain (Nd. Lausitz): 1937.

Dozy, R. P. A., and Englemann, W. H. *Glossaire des mots espagnols et portugais dérivés de l'arabe.* Leiden: 1869.

Eastwick, Edward B. *The Anvár-i Suhailí.* Hartford: 1934.

Egualiz y Yanguas, L. de. *Glosario etimológico de las palabras españolas . . . de origen oriental.* Granada: 1886.

Espinosa, A. M. "Notes on the Origin and History of the Tar-Baby Story." *Journal of American Folklore* XLIII:129 ff.

"Fables of Wisdom." *Putnam's Magazine* July 1868:77-84.

Fernández Llera, Víctor. *Gramática y vocabulario del Fuero Juzgo.* Madrid: 1929.

Flügel, G. L., ed. *Kitab al-Fihrist.* Leipzig: 1871-72.

Fuero de Usagre. Madrid: 1907.

Gabrielli, Francesco. "Kalilah e Dimnah." Enc. Italiana.

——————————. "L'opera de Ibn al-Muqaffaʿ". *Riv. degli studi orientali,* 1932.

Galmés de Fuentes, A. *Influencias sintácticas y estilísticas del árabe en la prosa medieval castellana.* Madrid, 1966.

Gammilscheg, Ernst. *Etymologisches Wörterbuch.* Heidelberg: 1928.

García Solalinde, A. *Calila y Dimna.* Madrid: 1917.

——————————. "Intervención de Alfonso X en al redacción de sus obras." *RFE* 1915.

Gayangos, Pascual de. *Escritores en prosa anteriores al siglo XV.* (*CeD* constitutes Part I.)

Georgiev, Vladimir. *Das Verbot im Griechieschen, Lateinischen, Bulgarischen, Altindischen, und der Injunktiv.* Sofia: 1935.

Girardin, S.-M. *La Fontaine el les fabulistes.* Paris: 1876.

González Palencia, Ángel. *Historia de la literatura arábigo-española.* Barcelona, 1928.

Guidi, Ignazio. *Studii sul testo arabo del libro di Calila e Dimna.* Rome: 1873.

Harris, Joel Chandler. *The Tar-Baby.* New York: 1904.

Herbelot de Molainville, B. de. *Bibliothèque orientale.* Paris: 1697.

Hertel, Johannes. *Das Pañchatantra.* Leipzig: 1914.

Hervieux, A. L. *Les fabulistes latins,* 5 vols. Paris. 1893-99.

Honeyman, A. M. *The Misison of Burzoe in the Arabic Kalilah and Dimnah.* Chicago: 1936.

Hottinger, A. *Kalila und Dimna—ein Versuch zur Darstellung der arabische-altspanischen Übersetzungskunst.* Bern, 1958.

Joly, A. *Histoire de deux fables de La Fontaine.* Paris, 1877.

Keith-Falconer, I. G. N. *Kalilah wa Dimnah.* Cambridge, 1885.

Keller, John Esten, and Linker, Robert W., eds. *El libro de Calila e Digna.* Madrid: CSIC, 1967.

Keniston, H., ed. *Fuero de Guadalajara*. Princeton: 1924.

Khalīl al-Yāziji. *Kalilah wa-Dimnah*. Beirut: 1888.

Knatchbull, Wyndham. *Kalila and Dimna, or the Fables of Bidpai*. Oxford: 1819.

La Fontaine, Jean de. *Fables*. Edited by G. Michaut. Paris: 1927.

Lancereau, Ed. *Hitopadésa ou l'Instruction utile*. Paris: 1925.

Lanchetas, Rufino. *Gramática y vocabulario de las obras de Gonzalo de Berceo*. Madrid: 1900.

Lerch, Eugen. *Spanische Sprach und Wesenart (Handbuch der Spanienkunde)*. Frankfurt a.M.: 1932.

Llorens, Eduard L. *La negación en español antiguo*. Madrid: 1923.

Lombard, Alf. "Die Bedeutungsentwicklung zweier ibero-romanischer Verba." *ZRPh* 1936.

Menéndez Pidal, Ramón. *Cantar de Mío Cid*, 3 vols. Madrid, 1908-11.

Menéndez y Pelayo, Marcelino. *Orígenes de la novela*, vol. 1. Madrid: 1905.

Meyer-Lübke, Wilhelm. *Romanisches etymologisches Wörterbuch*. Heidelberg: 1915-20.

Miquel, André, translator. *Le Livre de Kalila et Dimna*. Paris: Klincksieck, 1957.

Montiel, Isidoro. *Historia y bibliografía del libro de Calila y Dimna*. Madrid, 1975.

Morel-Fatio, A. "Recherches sur le texte et les sources du Libro de Alexandre." *Romania* IV:30.

Müller, Max. *Chips from a German Workshop*, vol. 4. New York: 1887.

Nöldeke, Theodor. *Burzoes Einleitung zu dem Buche Kalilah wa-Dimnah*. Strassburg, 1912.

——————. "Zu Kalila waDimna." *ZDMG* 1905.

Nykl, A. R. "Pícaro." *Revue Hispanique* 1929.

Oelschläger, Victor. *A Medieval Spanish Word-List*. Madison: 1940.

Paris, Gaston. "Les manuscrits de Kalilah et Dimna de Jean de Capoue." *Journal des Savants* 1899.

Pérez, Raoul M. *Vocabulario clasificado de Kalila et Digna*. Chicago: 1943.

Puymaigre, Th. J. P. de. *Vieux auteurs castillans*, 2 vols. Paris: 1888-90.

Rico y Sinobras, Manuel, ed. *Alfonso X el Sabio: Libros del saber de astronomía*, vol. 1. Madrid: 1863.

Robert, A. C. M. *Fables inédites*, 2 vols. Paris: 1825.

Rodríguez de Castro, Joseph. *Biblioteca española*, 2 vols. Madrid: 1781-86. Vol. 1 p. 636; vol 2. p. 625 ff.

Ryder, Arthur W. *The Panchatantra*. Chicago: 1925.

Sacy, Silvestre de. *Calila et Dimna*. Paris: 1816.

Sarmiento, Martín. *Mamorias para la historia de la poesía y poetas españoles*, vol. 1. Madrid, 1775.

Simonet, Francisco Javier. *Glosario de voces ibéricas*. Madrid, 1888.

Smith, C. Alphonso. *Southern Literary Studies*. Chapel Hill: 1927.

Sprengling, Martin. "Kalilah Studies I." *AJSL* 1923-24.

Steiger, Arnold. "Contribución a la fonética del Hispano-árabe." *RFE* 1932.

Steinschneider, M. *Die arabische Literatur der Juden*. Frankfurt: 1902.

——————. "Zur Geschichte der Übersetzung aus dem Indischen in's Arabische." *ZDMG* 1870.

Straparola, Giovanfrancesco. *Le piacevoli notti*, 2 vols. Bologna: 1899-1908.

——————. *The Facetious Nights*, 4 vols., with analysis of sources. Edited by W. G. Waters. London: 1901.

Vossler, Karl. *La Fontaine und sein Fabelwerk*. Heidelberg: 1919.

Ward, H. L. D. *Catalogue of Romances in the Department of Manucripts of the British Museum*, 2 vols. London: 1883-93. Vol. 2, pps. 149-181.

Wilkinson, J. V. S. *The Lights of Canopus*. London: 1929.

Wright, W. *The book of Kalilah and Dimnah*. London: 1884.

Printed in the United States
25719LVS00004B/118-165

9 781588 710734